'Ace Face' wann_____ made. At the Fr_____ _____ _____ _____, the most shaggable girl in Walsall, invites him to her home on the notorious Jerome K. Jerome estate. But will the woman of his dreams and a 'real' saddlemaker's job in the Happy Stallion make Mac the man he wants to be?

Take a cast list that includes demented Billy-Bob and his twizzler parents, sociopathic Tezza, a boy named Sue, and Brainy Kev, red-wine drinker and swot. Add a pet scorpion and an overdressed Yorkshire terrier to this Black Country brew, vintage 1979, and a pacy comic nightmare takes over.

Whispers in the Walls
New Black & Asian Voices from Birmingham
edited by Leone Ross & Yvonne Brissett
0 9535895 5 2

'The beautiful language of real people. These stories have integrity, sharpness and clarity. This is the real deal.'
Benjamin Zephaniah

'This powerful and moving collection does what the best short stories should do – provide a mirror into a less familiar world.'
Bonnie Greer

'Here are the voices of people who were seeded in this soil, voices utterly British, but resonating of the new Britain they are helping to make. I found the various writers compelling and completely unpredictable. A book which is so alive it feels hot to hold.'
Yasmin Alibhai-Brown

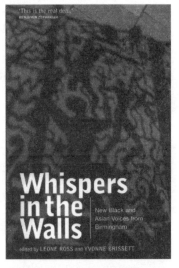

Tindal Street Press

217 The Custard Factory,
Gibb Street,
Birmingham B9 4AA
tel 0121 773 8157
fax 0121 693 5525
email info@tindalstreet.org.uk
website www.tindalstreet.org.uk

Volume 4 Autumn 2001

Editors: Julia Bell, Anna Garry, Esther Morgan, Vic Sage,
Ashley Stokes and Sara Wingate Gray
Contributing Editor: Peter Bush
Copy Editing: Emma Hargrave
Typesetting: Julian p Jackson
Subscriptions and Marketing: Simon Brett
For subscriptions and advertising contact: info@penandinc.co.uk

Pretext Editorial Board: Ian McEwan, Patricia Duncker, Andrew
Motion, Jon Cook, W.G. Sebald, Michèle Roberts.

Thanks to the following people for making this magazine possible:
The Arts Council of England, Jon Cook and Val Striker at UEA, the
Centre for Creative and Performing Arts and the Arthur Miller Centre,
UEA, the Esmée Fairbairn Charitable Trust, the Robert Gavron
Foundation, the John Jarrold Trust, Emma Hargrave at Tindal Street
Press, everyone at Signature, and all our contributors for allowing us to
publish their work.

Pretext is a Pen&inc publication for EAS Publishing, 2001
Pen&inc, English and American Studies, University of East Anglia,
Norwich, NR4 7TJ

ISBN: 1-902913-11-6

Pretext is published by Pen&inc at the University of East Anglia and
distributed by Signature Books, Sunhouse, 2–4 Little Peter Street,
Manchester, M15 4PS admin@signature-books.co.uk Tel: 0161 834 8767

Printed and bound by Biddles Ltd, Woodbridge Park, Guildford.

BLOODAXE BOOKS

ESTHER MORGAN was born in 1970 in Kidderminster. After reading English at Newnham College, Cambridge, she worked as a volunteer at the Wordsworth Trust in Grasmere, Cumbria. She took an MA in Creative Writing at the University of East Anglia and has since taught on its under-graduate creative writing programme, editing the UEA new poetry anthology *Reactions*. In 1998, she won an Eric Gregory Award, and taught at Edith Cowan University in Perth, Australia. *Beyond Calling Distance* is her first book of poems.

Esther Morgan

BEYOND CALLING DISTANCE

Esther Morgan's poems travel great distances across huge landscapes, both real and metaphorical: the big skies and endless horizons of the English Fens, the dust and rock of the Moon, the seas and deserts of dreams.

Out of these distances, voices speak, or try to speak, wanting to bridge the gap, to connect, to be heard as well as to listen. Many of her characters are isolated people: the woman taken in adultery, a traveller lost in the Australian outback, a suicide waiting to be discovered the survivors of war.

Balancing doubt with faith in language, these figures in a landscape depict themselves and the strange worlds they inhabit in sensuous detail. Beyond calling distance, at the edge of the audible, Esther Morgan's delightfully elusive poems await their reader.

'Esther Morgan's poems are full of hints and mysteries. They dance on sensuous feet while keeping a troubled eye on the music that keeps them dancing. But there are joys here as well as anxieties, and it is the two that amplify each other into such clear, poignant and resonant shapes' – GEORGE SZIRTES

To order a copy of Esther Morgan's *Beyond Calling Distance*, please send a cheque made payable to "Bloodaxe Books" for £7.95 to Unit 11, Penllyn Workshops, Plassey Street, Bala, Gwynedd, LL23 7SW. (Free post and packing)

THE
SERIOUS GAME
by
Hjalmar Söderberg

A literary sensation
at the age of 28 when
his first novel was
accused of being
pornographic,
Hjalmar Söderberg
was a rough
contemporary of
August Strindberg,
and one of
Scandinavia s most
prominent modernist
authors.

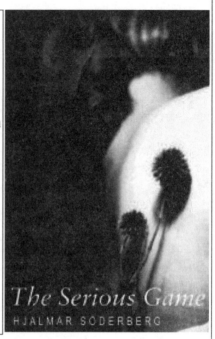

The Serious Game

HJALMAR SÖDERBERG

A work of tremendous insight, tenderness and gentle irony,
The Serious Game tells a compelling story of bright young
bohemians in love and struggling to free themselves from the
snares of liberal society.

Price: £8.99
Format: Paperback
ISBN: 0-7145-3061-1
Publication date: 24 September 2001
Distribution: Central Books Tel: 020 8986 4854 Fax: 020
8533 5821
Publicity: Catheryn Kilgar riff, Marion Boyars Publishers,
 24 Lacy Road, London, SW15 1NL

Contents

Ashley Stokes
Introduction

Havoc reigns when the rules break down, when consensus
collapses and chaos ensues. In the Middle Ages, the word
had an essentially military meaning. The cry havoc was a call to
pillage, when an army ran amok, massacred without pity or
quarter. Havoc was the moment when the dogs of war were let
slip, when the weak and pious were slaughtered, when women
and children were not first but next. Havoc means atrocity,
astonishment, violence and tragedy, the antithesis of civilization.
But as Amaia Gabantxo says in her introduction to this volume's
selection of poems by the Basque writer Jose Luis Padrón
Plazaola, 'societies in the midst of violent conflict are a
particularly fertile seedbed for beautiful poetry.' So havoc can be
seen as one of literature's great themes and triggers. By bringing
nations and community into conflict, by putting lives on the line,
by making personal moral choice a matter of greater social
significance, crisis and turmoil are a mainstay of fiction and
poetry, and have been from *The Iliad* to the brace of
contemporary novels set during the two world wars.

During the last week of August 2001 I sat down in my narrow,
airless office at the University of East Anglia and wrote an
introduction to Pretext 4, an issue we had decided to call 'Havoc'.
I argued that stability produces writers, not chaos. And the
world, I wrote, is a much safer place in 2001 than in the 19th and
20th centuries, with fewer wars than at any time since 1939. I
repeated Milan Kundera's idea from *The Book of Laughter and
Forgetting*, that stability has a negative effect on literature.
Everyone has so much time on their hands that they want to be

writers. There's 'a high enough degree of general well-being to enable people to devote their energies to useless activities'. In states in turmoil, however, a far smaller percentage of writers emerge. There are more important things to do.

Following this I suggested that a trip to one of our city centre bookshops would give fresh credence to Kundera's graphomania thesis. The shelves are full of books about routine lifestyle issues. Sweep and danger are largely found in novels set in the past. Much of our contemporary writing, I suggested, takes as its theme not the impact of havoc on societies and individuals, but the fallout from poverty, status-seeking and loneliness. A society without outside threats, especially a globalized consumer society without an emphasis on the family or collective identity, atomizes, inhibits community and engenders loneliness. And loneliness, according to Milan, encourages us to write, which in turn makes us lonelier still. Hence the tendency in the 1990s for novels about turning thirty, boys rites of passage, girls nights out and nostalgia for the recent past and its popular culture, novels on a small scale with nothing at stake.

I concluded by asking if isolation and atomization were not forms of havoc. Could they not be seen as 21st century havoc? I then surveyed the writers who have contributed to Pretext 4. Some have written about violent conflict and unstable relationships. Several explore the chaos of illness and the fear of bodily decay. The surrealists contained here break the rules of formal convention. Our lead piece, Lars von Trier's diary from the making of *The Idiots*, expresses a need for the artist to control havoc. Lastly, I drew attention to Lawrence Norfolk's essay 'Speech of the Weather': Writer's in Transit, which makes a case for writers to spend more time actively pursuing havoc and less time swanning about in hotels for marketing and promotional purposes. Norfolk suggests writers spend more time exploring 'exposed terrain', listening to 'the speech of the weather.' 'After the sterile comfort of a thousand hotel rooms,' he concludes, 'perhaps it is time to once again get wet.'

At the end of my first introduction to Pretext 4: Havoc I glibly hoped it might make you 'wet'.

The writing of that first version was the last task I undertook this summer. Shortly afterwards I made my first transatlantic flight and took my first holiday in eleven years. I flew to Toronto and stayed with my cousin and her husband. I then travelled to Peterborough, Ontario, where an old friend now lives with his wife and daughter. On September 11th, I was called out of the shower because Manhattan had been attacked. A joke, I thought, ha ha, and sloshed off to dry my hair. Downstairs, I realized that this wasn't a joke. Several days later, after days of 24 hour TV news and the shock and the fear, the disbelief and the despair, the speculation and the calls for revenge that bordered on bloodlust, I realized that my introduction to Havoc was both woefully inadequate and pitifully complacent. Havoc had reasserted itself mercilessly. It had changed the world. We are now living in a state where anything can happen. Nothing can be taken for granted. People are talking about ten years of war, of escalations, realignments, air raids, casualties. There's a whole new phraseology being born, a new vocabulary specific to now: 'asymmetrical conflict', 'infinite justice,' 'ground zero,' ground hero,' 'emotional correctness.' The comment section of the New Yorker talked of a civilizational calamity. Everything has changed. Everything changed in the two weeks after I wrote my first draft of this piece.

This is unlike any other peace time atrocity. Everyone is involved. The attack on the World Trade Center forces us to re-evaluate everything that we love in our lives, because the only way we can empathize with the bereaved and the murdered is by imagining that terrible circumstance visited upon ourselves. Everything now seems vulnerable. Everything seems fragile. Everyone seems transient, unreliable, cherished. But the images, the jetliners crashing into the towers, are eerily permanent. Every time you are forced to witness them again it is as if you are seeing them for the first time. On my return flight, as I peered out of the window at the golden circuit-board of the Greater Toronto Area as it receded below us, all I could picture was the image of jetliners hitting the WTA, as if the action were behind me, reflected on the glass. The images are impossible to escape or soften.

Introduction

It is now September 24th and the world is mobilizing for war. I do not now know whether this is an adequate or appropriate introduction to a volume about havoc. I do not want to write about havoc. I don't want to write at all. There are more important things to do.

I no longer hope that Pretext 4 will make you wet. I hope you are safe and dry.

Ashley Stokes
Norwich, 2001

Lars von Trier
Extracts from *The Idiots: A Film Diary*
Translated by Peter Holm-Jensen

Introduction by Peter Holm-Jensen

The following is part of a film diary which the Danish director Lars von Trier spoke into a dictaphone during the shooting of his 1998 Dogma film *The Idiots*. It was transcribed by a secretary and published, unedited, by von Trier himself. It appeared in a book which also contains the script and stills from the film. This book and the film are components of the same project.

Lars von Trier is one of the most important living film directors. He has been the main creative force behind the influential Dogma '95 movement. This is a Danish-born, but now worldwide project, whose stated aim is to eschew the conventions of Hollywood cinema in favour of a more 'immediate' form of expression (for instance, by using hand-held cameras). From the beginning, however, Dogma has related ambiguously to Hollywood conventions and to its own ideal of immediacy. These ambiguities are intensely present in the diary.

The film *The Idiots* is about a group of people who try to rid themselves of the trappings of civilization by acting out their 'inner idiots'. This they do by 'spassing', behaving like spastics, by giving free reign to repressed emotions and by transgressing most social conventions (as in the notorious group sex scene).

This diary is an outpouring of the emotional turmoil associated with making the film and interacting with the actors. It's a passionate, scurrilous, funny, cynical, deeply personal text.

The Idiots is also a film that contributed to the recent revolution of film censorship laws in Britain. This is one of the reasons why the diary is an important cultural document that requires an English translation.

Translated text

Preface

The following is a kind of diary which I recorded on a dictaphone throughout a period from just before the start of production until well into the editing stage. In keeping with the spirit of Dogma, I have neither read through nor corrected the text. However, Peter Øvig has been kind enough to read it and make corrections where they were necessary in order to make the spoken language readable – but without my intervention or censure.

Without otherwise disavowing the text, I will merely note that all statements are unprepared and thus spontaneous. Since both the factual and analytical information probably contain quite a few inaccuracies (not to say untruths), it is advisable to read the text as a kind of self-therapy on the part of the author, born out of the agitated emotional state that was the very technique of the film.

Lars von Trier, March 1998

*

It's the **29.5.** and there's a kind of calm before the storm as far as Dogma is concerned. I can't really pull myself together to do anything. I've thought a bit about the music, about finding some simple, childlike piece of classical music that can be played on the Pianola – at last free from rights. And I've talked about the sound with Per Streit, who's the sound engineer, and impressed on him the importance of each camera having a separate track, according to the Dogma rules. Apart from that, we talked about the fact that it's actually pretty inspiring to have to decide on location whether a scene is going to be silent, or what the sound in general will be like in the finished film. We talked about recording some sounds on location that you would normally create later on – these rules give you a very pure way of thinking. On Monday I start with the actors.

I was out canoeing yesterday and was attacked by an angry swan that sort of dove down towards me and finally boarded the canoe by jumping into the back of it. It was almost as if it was trying to capsize it, and I of course tried to retaliate with aggression. This was clearly unwise, but at least I got out of it alright. Maybe it was something of a symbolic meeting: if you see the swan as the actors and me in my unstable little canoe with my ass in the water . . . well, we'll see what happens. But I must admit I've got a lot of confidence in it at the moment. To stay with the symbolic, wasn't there something about Zeus being a swan when he impregnated Leda, who incidentally was a goose at that point. Well, there's something to think about.

Today is the **7.6.** and we've just had a week with the actors, sometimes one at a time, sometimes more . . . People have more or less started to spass, and it actually looks better than I thought it would, I must admit. The actors have been to a home or a workshop and are now being further briefed at various hospitals, or whatever we can find.

I've reached for the dictaphone in a humble attempt to keep up the diary. I'll say that I'm in a pretty good mood today, and the weather's wonderful, and we've got the kids, and yes, I'm pretty keen . . . What else can I say? We've discussed with great enthusiasm the necessity of including several erect members and various penetrations in the film. We've discussed several solutions, as a last resort getting some of Trine Michelsen's friends from the harder part of the industry to supply the close-ups. Everyone seems to be taking this side of the affair with relatively good humour, which of course is fantastic. On the whole, I have to say everything is pretty merry at the moment.

We were at the villa for the first time the day before yesterday with Jens Albinus and Bodil and Anne Louise. Everyone was glad to see the place. The advantage of having a place like that is of course that it becomes a kind of home, and everyone was happy and thought 'this is where we live', and 'oh look, here's a little room, and here . . .' It's exactly like moving into a house you're going to live in, and I think it's very good for the communal idea to have a place like that. It . . . well, it makes me very happy.

I've more or less abstained from dissecting my shit. The only disheartening thing is that I've now started looking for tumours in my scrotum . . . I've sort of stopped now, but it's been a pretty agonized time. Now I'm running a bath for little Agnes. And Bente is getting enormous.

The **10.6.** We had the first actor day in the villa yesterday, and it was very good. Everyone got a chance to tell what they knew about their character. It worked sort of theatrically, and I sense a lot of enthusiasm . . . Bodil, who's playing Karen, of course started crying when she was telling the whole group about her character. They're all identifying with their characters to such a extent that it almost shines through stronger in the private sphere. It's all exciting and invigorating and encouraging, so . . . yes, I'm looking forward to this with great pleasure. You can't avoid feeling very closely related to kindergarten teachers and the like.

25.6. Ecstatic film joy! Yes, that probably covers it . . . We started by shooting the taxi scene, where Karen drives from Søllerød Inn out to Rockwool, however absurd that sounds. We couldn't shoot these first days in chronological order, though we'd hoped to do the whole movie that way – not that that's a Dogma rule at all. But we started with that scene, and it surpassed all expectations. The very important moment when Henrik and Stoffer have to leave the spassing mode and become normal people and Karen's reaction to it I thought turned out well. Since there wasn't room for the cameraman in the car, I drove it, and the actors filmed each other on some of the settings. It worked well, and it was a fun idea for them to film each other.

Afterwards we went to the forest and shot a fantastic scene, which turned out completely Fellinian. I broke with the Dogma rule about not having any aesthetics and sprinted over to that part of my childhood's forest . . . it's a strange part, because I've used almost all the forests and streams and God knows what out here, but precisely this part of the forest, which I think of as the most poetic and almost Japanese-inspired part, I've never used. I naturally steered towards it, as I'd do on any ordinary walk, and it's a tiny little pine wood with green grass on the ground, and we were blessed with a windy day. The scene was originally meant to be shot in the sunshine, with Nana lying down sunning herself, so it only gets funnier when she asks for suntan lotion on a shitty grey day – it gets even more absurd to rub mayonnaise all over yourself, and all that.

Apart from that, afterwards we got a fantastic poetry out of moving the conversation that didn't work the other night, from inside, where it didn't belong, to out here, with this fantastically high ceiling. It was inspiring somehow, and all those loonies walking around, it was actually – I haven't thought about this before now – it was actually Truffaut's *Fahrenheit* something or other, where they walk around in the forest memorizing books, and it's beautiful as hell, of course. So the loonies were walking around each in his or her own way, while Karen and Stoffer discussed and talked, and it really got a very very great poetry, for example thc line where he says 'in the Stone Age all the idiots died, but it doesn't have to be like that anymore'. It got a great poetry when the shot simultaneously panned out over all the idiots, especially Ped, who was in the wheelchair, it was just very beautiful and fantastically naive and sentimental and everything all at once. You might say those are the kinds of gifts you get along the way. Things you wouldn't have written in a manuscript because it would be over the top, you suddenly get as a gift, and that's allowed. That's actually what all the Dogma rules are about – that you can allow yourself a lot of things precisely because of the rules. And it turned out fucking great, that scene.

Then we tried to work a bit creatively with the sound for the first time, that's to say we stuck the microphone in the treetops and got the wind in the treetops over loads of shots of the spassers just walking around, so we don't hear their real sound, just the treetops. And it's so so so over the top, an over the top cinematic cliché, which I've otherwise shied away from, but which suddenly, because we had to make the decision on the spot, became real and worked fucking brilliantly. Well, that's what I think now, anyway, without having seen it. I was almost moved when Josephine and Jeppe touch each other while they're spassing. The funny thing about this film is that it only takes a milligram of love in some little corner, and you're . . . and you break down in convulsive sobbing. Maybe it's just my brain that's totally hyperactive, but that's how I feel . . .

It's a film that's a lot less calculating than *Breaking*, and yet far far far far more calculating. Well, that might be hard to understand, not more calculating, but much more . . . I don't know . . . allowing yourself to go on an effects-picnic with many many nods to Widerberg and Truffaut and Tarkovsky and kiss my ass. But it was fucking beautiful, and . . . when I was filming there, I cried, and on the way home I cried too, the soft little man in his stupid giant mobile home listening to the Spice Girls. And then I get – I can hardly bring myself to say this, but I guess a diary demands some sort of honesty – then I get so maudlin and suddenly afraid for . . . my talent. Well, this really isn't easy to listen to, I'm totally aware of that, but when you've done a scene like that – and that's why I'm talking about the ecstatic – you get scared that there's some big big hubris that'll drop down from the sky like a giant fist and squash you like one of those mosquitoes from the forest. I thought, 'surely I'll get cancer now, surely I'll get cancer now'. There's no way out once you get to that point. And it may be that we've achieved nothing today, but still the feeling is intact. I'm thinking, 'for chrissake, I'm brilliant, I'm brilliant, I'm brilliant'. I'm brilliant, and it'll be interesting to see this in print when the film comes out and it gets the finger. But I still think that for the sake of the cause I have to say it as it is – that on the way home I thought 'jesus, this is really rolling . . . jesus, you can really do this shit, you can really set these things free'.

I thought of Per Streit, who was genuinely enlivened by it. He is really as uptight as they come, but even he could see that he had to do Dogma too. Although he's the biggest sound aesthetician in Denmark and teacher at the Film School and all that, he could still see that it's fun to have to go out and mix your sound on the spot, to put in the music and take leaves in the wind and lay it over people who are walking around and talking, and decide on the spot whether an image should be silent or not. To make those decisions out there on location is surely fucking fantastic. Who the hell else does that now? Nobody does! . . . Yes, this is an atrocious diary entry, but . . . sorry, but I needed to . . . I 'feel' it has to be said . . . feel should be read in quotes . . .

The **29.6.** I've taken the weekend off, and haven't slept very much. Just bloody amazing how I only sleep three hours at a time and then wake up, and it's not even because things are going particularly badly . . .

I had a chat with Jens about the dickshot, and I think I'll give a little speech tomorrow about solidarity and things like that, because although it's going well, it's of course important that everyone is clear about the aim. In that connection I'll also say why both the stiff dick and the penetration – which I hope to get with the help of some stand-ins – are important to me and not just childish, as they might seem to be. They're important to me, both because they give the film a roughness which it needs, and maybe a dangerousness too, which it also needs because it's so lightweight in some scenes. And because we had a consultant working on this, who works at Ebberødgård, and he said the retarded were very well portrayed, but that their sexuality was a bit missing. Of course, I'm perfectly aware that sexuality is a big part of many of the characters, or should be, and especially the exaggerated uninhibited sexuality is an important part. That's why it's important to me to include that aspect of it too, because to make a film about the retarded without including that fact, that's like . . . well, yes, pietistic literature about sex. I mean, you have to get the whole picture, otherwise it's worthless. The kind of retarded people we've chosen in this film don't go around constantly jerking off on the street, but that aspect of the characters and this life and that way of being has to be included too! In that regard I have to say once again I think it was fantastic of Jens to get that dick up. Not a lot of people would have spent three hours and a beautiful, though somewhat drizzly Thursday afternoon on it . . .

11.7. . . . The day began well, I had Bodil, or Karen in the film, and Anne Louise, or Susanne in the film, alone in order to pick up on the much-discussed staircase scene, which has now been moved and takes place in a window frame, where they're sitting together,

7

and where there are actually only three or two lines. Karen is crying and says: 'I shouldn't be crying.' 'Why shouldn't you be crying?' 'No, I don't have the right. I don't have the right to be this happy,' and then Susanne says: 'You should be happy,' and then she cries, and it's after she's seen them spassing at some point. You'd think this was a very simple scene, and it's now the third or fourth day we've tried to get it right. My main criticism of the performances has been that I didn't think Susanne was credible. Bodil's shown a great sensitivity several times in this scene, I think, and there have also been tears in the right way, but she doesn't control them as precisely as I might have thought she would, and that's probably fine. But this time we recorded it over several hours, just talking and feeling our way into it, and I definitely think Bodil's done some good things and throughout the whole sequence has covered the things I wanted. But throughout I've felt that Susanne should have been able to do better, or that Anne Louise should have been able to do better. In this very intimate situation – and of course especially because it's been problematized by the fact that we've done it so many times – it sometimes happens that she starts listening to herself . . . whereas I normally think she delivers her lines wonderfully, when she doesn't think about them, naturally and very very very very precisely. It's a paradox that she wasn't able to do it here, or that I didn't think it quite measured up to my concept of authenticity. It may be that no one else in the world can hear or see it, or that it's completely wrong, but in any case I had that feeling, so we started the sequence with a long long long conversation, which I filmed by myself. We set up a microphone, and then we sat and filmed by ourselves, and the idea was for Susanne to talk about the parallels between Karen's and Susanne's problems, because Susanne is the one who's always taking care of other people in this film, and never gets thanked for it, and it's a bit like we imagine Karen's situation to have been from earlier on in the story, with the child and the family at home etcetera. In a way it had to do with a mirror effect, which I've talked about before. The intention was that Anne Louise should be allowed to tell about her problems, and by all means her grief and her longing and so on, so that some sort of understanding would arise between these two women each telling their own story.

But it was hard. She had a hard time getting into it, and then I said: 'Just speak as Anne Louise instead then'. And then she talked about her childhood for a long time, and all kinds of things, and then the little therapist in me awoke, because all the talks we have are always on the edge of the therapeutic, and I've also in my many years of experience with therapy – though seen from one of the two chairs, that is, set up for a gestalt purpose – picked up a thing or two. I think it's really fucking exciting, and I naturally encouraged her to open up and tell about it as well as she could. And to some extent she did, and at one point she says: 'It was hard to get enough space at home as a child, by the way'. And right when she said that little thing about space, right at the word space, she got a little tic, which was very small, but which I took note of. I thought, this must be what therapists do – before you're conscious of what you're doing, they observe, they listen and piece things together, and then they see what kinds of things are being said without being said, and in reality are unconscious. So I kept going and asked what she meant by not having enough space, and she answered evasively a few times, three or four times actually, and I thought the technique must be to stick to it again and again. And when I asked her for the fourth time, she suddenly broke down completely and sobbed like a madwoman and afterwards talked for a long time about her childhood and about the feeling of not being able to live up to demands, and the lack of space and understanding. It was very very moving and lovely and liberating for all of us. But to cut out the sentimental bits, it resolved the scene, because when we did it afterwards, Bodil turned out fine – but it's clear she gets a bit flooded or swamped by Anne Louise's story . . .

It's the **13.7.** and it's a Sunday . . . I wake up three or four times a night these days, and it's been mostly positive, all this energy, as opposed to waking up with cancerfear . . . When I woke up I felt I had so much to say to this little tape, but now I'm having trouble remembering it. One thing is certain: the production and the work with the actors and the whole situation is so pleasurable at the moment that it affects me privately too. I've never been able to see the beauty in . . . the bodily aspects of pregnancy, but

The Idiots: A Film Diary

I have to admit that when I come home from work, sweet sweet Bente beams at me almost . . . excuse the expression, but almost provocatively, and that's . . . well, that's kind of interesting in regard to all the emotions associated with the production.

I remember Bergman says somewhere that the greatest pleasure of his career was a time he shot a scene with twenty or thirty policemen, and talked to them through a megaphone, telling them how to behave. It was the most satisfying thing he'd ever done, naturally because of his fear of the authorities, and I've experienced something similar in Poland with the Red Army, which at that time was still the Red Army: I could distribute them at will and ask them to do various things. In a sense you might say that this production, precisely because it's Danish, and with . . . yeah, a bunch of friends like these, somehow compensates for childish or youthful defeats in relation to other people. I feel that strongly, and that's definitely deeply satisfying. I don't know if it's having power over people that's satisfying – in any case it's satisfying that it's my game we're playing. And of course deeply frustrating when any of them question my ownership of the game. Incidentally, Troels called the other day with a guilty conscience, which I thought was a beautiful and endearing trait. And then you can think about how primitive your perception of other people really is, deep down.

But maybe it's also precisely my happiest moment because it's a Danish film, and that somehow gives me extreme satisfaction. And that it's basically . . . well, that I basically have a freedom that perhaps I've never allowed myself before. It's wonderful that the Dogma rules have chucked aesthetics out the window. And still a scene like the one we did in the window frame with those two girls gets all kinds of traces of *Persona* and God knows what, and it's fine, because it's born out of the situation itself, and it's not adapted in any way.

And I'm not really sure what the fucking date is . . . it's the **15.7.**. and it's half past two at night, no, twenty to three, and as usual I can't sleep. I came home from the shooting, went to bed at twelve, dead tired, and now of course I can't sleep. I've drunk vodka and taken sleeping pills, and I . . . oh fuck off. It's too fucking stupid!

We've done some shooting with Michael Moritzen today, The Local Authority Man, and it was a huge piece of work. We've covered it quite well, I think. We need to do a little reworking tomorrow. The most sensational thing today was actually the spassing with real caviar, and our dear spassers spit out six thousand kroner worth of Iranian caviar, which somehow affected them all, including me. To spit it out again was, at least the first time they did it, possibly the most provocative thing you could do in this film. But interesting! They attacked the incredibly good wines and the good food so ferociously that Anne-Grethe had to go out and be sick afterwards. Otherwise it's gone well, and now I'm lying here tossing and turning, and I shouldn't be. I don't know . . . it's all whirling around in my head, and after the weekend I was actually a lot calmer after Anne Louise, but now . . . now it's really fucking whirling around, and I don't want to be . . . now it's uncomfortable. I don't want her to be nice to me or nasty to me or anything at all. I just want everything to be over with this film, so I don't have to see her. And it's totally stupid, because she's just going about her . . . well, she's not doing anything at all. I'm the one who's getting myself totally overwrought. But now it's just got to a point where it's agonizing and stupid, and I'm lying here alone because Bente's in Tisville, and she shouldn't be. She should be here with me! It's completely ridiculous: who the hell does she think she is!? She should be lying here, so you could sort of snuggle up . . . I don't know . . . It's whirling around in my head too much. I just don't know what to think about anymore to make me calm down. As soon as I start thinking about the film I start editing it and . . . I guess it's some sort of Edgar Allan Poe thing about the mind being too sensitive. And that sounds really smart, but he did have a good short story about it, I remember. I can picture him dying in his delirium tremens, triggered by the too too too sensitive mind that whirled around in his skull all the time. No, I just have to survive these last couple of weeks. No matter what thought I try to focus on in my head, it's as if it becomes a burden. But you could say it's a good thing there isn't room for the anxieties on top of that, because then it would all be truly impossible – then you'd probably be insane.

But now we're finally nearing the end. I just want to say that the prelude to this film was among the easiest of them all, apart from the fact that writing the manuscript was a little agonizing – not the four days themselves, but what preceded it, because I didn't think I had anything apart from a good idea, which I couldn't pin anything on, because it was very abstract. It was agonizing to go around mulling it over without getting anything out of it, and now I feel I've had so much more than my fill of all these people. Some stupid film crush, it's too childish. I'm not even in love! It's not even reality, just something I'm making up in my skull, for Christ's sake. Apparently it's because in this situation and in this life you're lit up by some spark that makes it all whirl around your brain, round and round and round and round. You could say sensitivity is a tool, but it's bloody well not a tool that's very pleasant or easy to use. It's easy to understand why Bille August had to go out and screw every woman he saw – or whatever it is he's done. Somehow or other it must be . . . the same thing that can be so pleasurable is also agonizing. For fuck's sake . . . Bente, come home and lie here with me, goddammit!

Here comes the newspaper, it's three o'clock and I can't sleep, and I'll have to consider jerking off for the fifth time to fall asleep . . . My poor, poor, poor dick. For fuck's sake . . . !

16.7. . . . At midday we had Porn-Lasse and some other porn models in to supply some real dick-in-cunt for the middle of the orgy scene. The actors had already gone very far in their attempt to achieve something realistic . . . the spassing of lust. Ped surprised and impressed everyone by getting a fantastic hard-on, and Katrine impressed everyone by jerking it. Troels was also really good in his spasser character in the situation, and all in all everyone struggled bravely with the whole thing.

In the first take we did, people were disassociating themselves too much from it. The way this scene has developed, we've constantly removed the things you do to make it less dangerous, that is, laugh and make it childish or make it into something different from what it is. But then we got the porn models in, and it was really bloody difficult for the actors to be present. Actually, they only had to act the scene as they had done before, only with the porn models fucking in the corner, so we could pull a camera over the real thing once in a while and over to the others or have it take place in a corner. It was strangely strangely strangely difficult for the other actors. Troels switched off and couldn't do it. He started to, but couldn't and had to give up. And it was hard for Jens, he had to go for a walk. And it was hard for . . . it was bloody hard for everybody, and that surprised me a lot. When I compare it with my own perception or my own reaction to the people who were lying there really fucking, it was like, after four seconds you've got completely used to it. Seeing somebody fucking for real at a shooting doesn't affect you at all. It's not disgusting, it's not vulgar as in a porn film, not in the least. It's not sexually exciting, it's nothing! It's as though they were filing their nails. We filmed it for a long time and you're not affected by it in any way, and that's why I'm wondering why the actors reacted the way they did. At the same time you could see the models felt fine about what they were doing. They had no problems with it, they felt fine. You couldn't say they enjoyed it, I don't think they did, but at the same time they felt completely fine about it. It wasn't a problem for them at all. So it was strange, why this aversion arose, and why it was so unpleasant. They struggled with it, Anne Louise struggled to stay there, everyone struggled. It was big and difficult, but they did it, and it was good, because the shots as I can see now, are essential to the scene. They're exactly the ones that give it back that dangerousness that makes it impossible for you to disassociate yourself from it. It's dangerous. There are people who are playing at being retarded and at the same time really fucking. That gives the scene precisely that little transgressive element it needs, and this film needs. I think that's important at all times.

I talked to Jens on the phone a short while ago about why this happened. And he said it was hard to supply something that was only meant to be an effect, in other words a kind of background effect. But I don't understand the explanation, and I'll have to talk to him and the others tomorrow about what the hell it is that's so difficult. They were doing the exact same scene before, they were lying there fucking or pretending to be fucking, and everyone was happy about it and thought it was wonderful. Then these people come in and do it for real in a corner, and it shouldn't make any difference . . .

19.7. . . . Regarding my fascination with some of the girls, Jens said quite clearly that . . . well, that Anne Louise would naturally think you're wonderful, or would want to appear to think you're wonderful, also because . . . well, think about her situation, her private situation, and that she's an actress, so of course she'd say that at any given moment. It was good having a bucket of cold water dumped on you like that, and I've taken it to heart, and it's of course completely justified. Who could demand anything else, that's clear. Basically we haven't achieved a fucking thing in terms of intimacy or understanding. And that's fine, it's all a fictional plane after all, and maybe the only one who really really believes in it – or believed there was anything real in it – is me. And that's fair enough, that's how it is. We're entertainers, for God's sake, all of us. Fine, fine. It's just, how to put it, the hard school, that I have to relearn it every time. But you might also say that the technique is to believe in it. Clearly, when I direct I have to believe it's real. At any rate my point of departure must be that this is real, otherwise I can't judge it in any way, and that's why it's so goddamn difficult, and I become like a tiny tiny little child, and I understand that this isn't reality after all. It's acting, and it's a bunch of stilted crap and some constructs of a theoretical and dramaturgical nature. However much we want the dramaturgy to stay out of it, it's always still there. And it's some kind of game that little Lars from some grammar school class has staged, and it'll never have any reality because in a basic basic basic sense deep deep deep down you're one hundred and ninety thousand percent lonely in your own tiny tiny little stupid, ridiculous, humiliating world.

Bente on the other hand is wonderful and generous and buxom, and yes, that's . . . that's got to be a mirage. Today's PS must be that, as everyone knows, it's all about being loved and getting power, emotionally as well as physically. And when a day like yesterday could be completely destroyed because for some childish reason I feel unloved or unable to get hold of the love

I'm pining for in some completely trivial form, then it has to be said it approaches the howlingly unprofessional. When I move around in my little working situation with my emotions as a tool, like Jørgen Leth [filmmaker] would do with his curiosity, I can't help not giving a shit about film and not giving a shit about artwork and not giving a shit about a higher aim, as soon as the tiniest tiniest tiniest tiniest little thing goes wrong with some fucking . . . some fucking power shit, as Katrine would say.

The comparison between me and Stoffer in the film is becoming more and more howlingly grotesque, apart from the fact that the childishness in him is nothing compared to me or mine. The lie between the actors and me or people in general is also portrayed too too kindly in this film, as in the others. It's all howlingly banal in any case, and deeply two-faced. How could I even dream of getting an honest answer to anything at all from a group of career-hungry young actors, either of a professional or personal kind?

Somehow it takes me completely back to my youth, where I'm sitting in the corner of a party, raging at not being able to step into any kind of community feeling and not getting any kind of girls and not getting any of my frustrations soothed at all. Because who the hell can see me for what I am and for what I want? I won't even answer that. And it wouldn't make it any less laughable if I were to express an observation about my sensitivity being a kind of jester's tool, about the agonizing . . . I'm constantly trying to find another word than 'honesty', which is a bit too Bergmanesque, but I'm having trouble thinking of one while the tape is running, so let's just call it an agonizing honesty, with all the reservations you can think up. The conclusion I wanted to reach – now I can't even remember the beginning of my sentence – naturally had to do with the fact that nobody's interested in it, and that's the plain truth. And in a gigantic scream for contact and love you shovel out adolescent honesty, which only makes everything worse, and you're left even more lonely than before . . . yeah, sorry the sarcasms are missing today . . .

Claire MacDonald
Lightly Smashed

We leave our marks on houses. Scuffs, smears, hair, blood. A dent in the floor, a stain on the bed, broken windows, forced locks. Signs of struggle. I could tell a story just by listing those marks.

In those days we needed stories. All the stories we told were things that really happened, all the names were names of real people, but they were not all about us and they didn't all happen to us. That is how it was. We needed stories to remind us of who we were. At other times we did other things, were other people even. But that was somewhere else and this was now, always.

There were twelve of us that summer and the house we lived in was called the Colgate house. It stood in the grounds of an art college from which everyone else had disappeared to France or Greece by the end of July. I was teaching theatre there and the house came with the job. It was huge and white, a beached ocean liner more suited to Malibu than Dorset. A once elegant Bauhaus house, built for a German choreographer in the 1930s and now faded by rain, speckled with green mould and streaked with dirt. It had huge light rooms, almost bare but for bits of secondhand furniture and books. It was covered in vines. It had a dance studio and balconies where we slept. The long garden was in front of a field that sloped down to the river where we kept our boat. It had wood fires and sheds full of the toys of previous families. Marks on the doorframes recorded the heights of long grown-up children. Miles from town, it was like a deserted playground. In the late afternoons we would walk back from the river through the college grounds, around the deserted swimming pool full of leaves, past empty buildings, their doors swinging open. At night it was pitch black. No street lights, no neighbours for miles. A house across the river occasionally occupied by a film director who lived in Spain. Apart from that, just us. A dark so soft and tangible, the river shone with a silvery luminescence and we would walk at midnight in the deep, wet grass and look up from the river bank at our house almost hidden by trees.

We were old friends. Some of us went back years, to university where we had lived in a series of shared houses in Leeds and then in London: Hyde Park Terrace, Grove Green Road, Spencer Place. Houses with shabby velvet curtains, damp cellars and gardens full of rusting metal and broken pots, where once we were students and then where we started food co-ops and theatre companies and held parties and had children. Ostensibly we were working together that summer. We were writing a film which ended up being quite big on the independent circuit at the end of the 1980s, called *Falling into the Light*, a sort of postmodern sci-fi thriller. I lived in the house with my kids during the week and the others – the composer, the director, some of the actors – would come down at weekends to work and to sail, and friends who were teachers or who were in between jobs just came and stayed.

We worked at night because our children were still small. Five or six among the dozen of us, blond ones and dark straggle-haired ones with dirty hands and faces who tagged along playing, swimming and sailing, poking fires out with twigs and drinking the dregs of margaritas from paper cups. I see them now, little naked figures wearing laurel crowns who came to us for orange squash, biscuits and for help removing splinters from their bare feet.

People came and went. We had some Americans rehearsing a dance piece; a couple of German acrobats preparing for a tour; a macrobiotic doctor who had cured herself of cancer; jazz musicians from Italy taking a break before flying to Japan. One of them was the father of one of the children, a tiny fair-haired girl who had been born in Italy. When he came to see her he played Bach on his cello in the old dance studio while the children danced, jumping and spinning, making strange shapes with their hands, wearing holey T-shirts and garlands of flowers.

To come across that house, in that place, was like falling

through a door into some other world in which things didn't mean the same, but once you were there you recognized where you were. It was like a place from a holiday you can barely recall where you met up with a couple of people you'd never met before and went off to a village you could never find again. And in that village you ate some soup you can still taste in dreams.

I know what you're thinking, and it's true. There is a carelessness to that life. It feeds on the story of itself as a charmed circle; there seems to be no need to tend its edges, to test its safety margins, to note who comes in and why. It's loose and improvised and – you think – safe, nothing can really happen there. But there is a kind of madness that comes from stretching the possible, from turning all days into the space when dreams happen between waking and sleeping. Perhaps you invite danger in, perhaps it is all just chance.

Neil first came to stay with us after he'd been climbing in Wales. Called one August afternoon, told us he was a friend of Ben's – or Matt's or Richard's – and asked if he could stay for a few days on his way home. That was how it was. Our house was on that kind of circuit. If you were a writer or a video artist or if you lived in the north of Spain and you were designing the lighting for a dance tour, or you just knew someone who was, you could ring us up and if it was convenient you came to stay. Neil was different. Very quiet. He'd had a couple of books published – one on climbing, one a travel guide – and he wrote for specialist magazines on things like new materials for hiking gear or advances in rope technology. He would write in the morning on his laptop and sleep naked all afternoon on the roof in the shade. He had beautiful skin. Sometimes I lay down beside him and he would fold his arm around me loosely and we would sleep together until I heard the kids and would get up to feed them, bathe them, quell a fight, and he would sleep on. It was a strange kind of intimacy, unspoken, unmentioned in the melée of everything else. He had a partner and a kid but he was taking a break, we never asked why. He left after a couple of weeks and I didn't hear from him until late autumn. He called one afternoon as I got home and said he had split up with his partner and could he come and stay.

Lightly Smashed

There had been a sense during that summer that time was infinite. That it stretched in different directions, that you could open a space in it, light a fire in that space and curl up and live in it. But as summer slid into autumn we were under pressure. The film was going into production and the director was also contracted to direct a musical about AIDs for a Theatre in Education company in Gwent. There'd been a train strike and we had had little time together to work. We had some Dutch people staying who were running a course in dance video, but I said we'd find room. It was late October: for me, the most romantic time of the year in England. A sense of both ending and beginning. Pungent smells, fading mauve light, that sort of thing. We'd made a vegetable garden in the spring and now we spent every spare moment making huge meals or pickling, bottling, storing. We still had the boat too, so we were sailing in the estuary and people would come down to sail with us, or we'd take the children out in the dinghy near the house and pretend to be pirates. But I was teaching as well and the house often felt dirty and damp, full of drying clothes and crying children.

It was funny with Neil. I wasn't sure why he wanted to come back. I picked him up from the station in my 2CV (he didn't drive), and he seemed smaller and even more silent. I think I must have felt quite, I don't know, protective somehow. I want to say maternal but it wasn't maternal, more controlling than that if I'm honest. He hadn't seemed entirely at home when he stayed with us before. In fact, he was quite disdainful. Sometimes he would give the impression that he'd seen it all before or that we were all privileged, bourgeois drop-outs, while he was a genuine writer with working-class roots, but he must have known we weren't drop-outs at all. We had jobs, kids, deadlines – but there was also some unspoken sense in which it was all a bit of a game, so that we could appear to be not working at all, just drinking and sailing and staying up late. But in the end, as if by magic, some beautifully made piece of work would arise out of a process which hid its difficulty underneath a veneer of clever hedonism. So many parties when some visiting theatre director or actress would say, 'Do you remember that bar in Valladolid where we had that amazing mussel dish?' and 'No, that was in Naples – God those dealers, I can't believe we got back alive,' or some other froth that was only half true. Neil and I used to go for silent walks, and I often had the impression that he wanted to tell me something but that he hadn't quite worked out how to say it. If he was in pain from the break-up, he never said. He simply kept it to himself.

We'd played a lot of games that autumn. If people came for the weekend or we were having tea in the evening with the children, we would play Scrabble, Uno or Poker if there were just three or four of us, but we would make up big games at the dinner table too. Like one night when we said – and there must have been eight or more of us and the children had gone to bed or were arguing in their own rooms – let's just go round and say all the jobs we have ever had, one at a time, and so we went round, each saying one. We began at thirteen and fourteen – babysitter and paperboy – and then fifteen, sixteen – waitress or washing cars – and then seventeen, eighteen – hitched to France and picked grapes, worked on a kibbutz, chambermaid in a hotel in Paris. And Neil would just say 'butcher's apprentice' for years and years and then not much else but 'writer, on the dole', 'writer, on the dole'. We laughed a lot: we imagined him apprenticed to some fat, red Midlands butcher in some horrible cold shop. He said it in this great deadpan way. But that was what he really did when he left school. I think he worked in a tobacconist's too at some point. It was very funny.

I'm trying to picture him as he was then. I remember his voice, of course, quite low and with a slight Midlands accent. He knew an awful lot of words. If we played Scrabble you wanted to be on his team. I don't know where they came from. He was always being challenged. He knew words like 'apodictic' and 'imbricated', obscure climbing terms and dialect words no one else knew.

Neil really looked after me that autumn and I wish I could thank him for that, in spite of everything. I was so stressed. It wasn't as easy as it looked, of course it wasn't. The house was always filthy. In the summer it didn't matter but in the winter we had to chop wood every day for the fires and it was wet and the children would drag mud in from the garden and the rooms were drafty and cold and the shops were miles away. He made me cups of tea and calmed me down. I was always behind with stuff. I was always trying to make space for myself and never could, and trying to do ten things at once – teach, write, look after kids. But we never slept together. Did I say I was a single parent? I think I left that out. Sounds so downtrodden. I'd had two daughters in my twenties with my Spanish lighting-designer boyfriend. He'd gone back to Spain and came over occasionally to work but basically I was on my own. I had the odd affair but I didn't sleep with Neil, I mean, after that kind of Platonic summer thing. I sort of knew not to.

After a couple of weeks I realized he had no plans to leave. He had some kind of commission to write another climbing book, and so he had a bit of money which he kept in the post office. He said he didn't like banks. He wasn't secretive in a furtive way, he just never said anything. The problem was that I seemed to have money. We'd had an advance on the film and so we were always buying crates of beer and wine and bottles of whisky. But personally I was quite hard up, although I felt too proud to say anything. We just carried on in the same shabby, faded chic sort of way we always had.

It was weird the way it happened, but as soon as it did I knew that I had known it would. I knew that in some way I had already dreamt it, already invoked it into being. It still makes me quite sick to think about it. I remember being incredibly tired. I must have had quite a lot to drink because I was deeply asleep. I also remember the house being dead quiet. The children had gone to stay with a friend on an organic farm up the road where they had horses, and I was on my own except for Neil. We'd stayed up late drinking whisky and he'd been really kind about some crisis I was going through, and we had hugged briefly and said goodnight. I wasn't aware of him coming into the room. The first thing I remember was hearing his breathing very close to me, and then half seeing him above me and realizing he was naked, and that he had an erection and a knife. And then he was coming closer, half whispering through gritted teeth, 'I'm going to fucking kill you.' He brought the knife very close, making little slashes in the air and I thought, 'Oh my God, he's going to cut my face,' but he just held the knife against my cheek and said, 'You don't get it, do you, what it is you do, you just don't get it.' I don't think I said anything at all, I'm sure I didn't, and he said, in a much quieter voice, 'Don't say a word, you've talked far too much already,' and he pulled the duvet off me and pulled up my nightdress. I thought at first he was going to rape me but instead he just looked at me and said, 'I love you, I love you. If you would just touch me, just really touch me, just once.' He kept shaking his head and by then I realized he was masturbating and I'm not sure what he said then, he had straddled my legs and he still had the knife in one hand. Then he came over my body. I could smell it very strongly, it was hot and then cold very quickly, and it felt like the whole room lurched and swam. He kind of groaned and inhaled very deeply and looked at me again and said, 'There. There,' and got up and left the room.

There were no locks on the doors. I didn't dare get up. I didn't know where he was but I didn't want to switch on the light. I just lay there and what went through my head were all those things I had said and done, and all the little mannerisms that he must have seen as flirting I suppose, and I remembered the way he had looked at me, and a long walk we had taken together when he had sat just too close to me and I had felt powerful. Here I was, a real risk taker. Unfettered by bourgeois convention. Good looking, sexy even. Intellectual, creative. Look but don't touch, Neil.

He was never going to hurt me, I know that now. I guess I knew it then. I didn't think I would sleep but I must have, eventually. I took off the nightdress, wiped my body and pulled the covers over me, naked and shivering with guilt and fear. It was late when I woke up and of course he was gone. A friend from London was coming down that day, not a friend I could tell. I just cleaned up and because I didn't tell her I sort of buried it and didn't tell anyone. I just said Neil had gone and he'd be in touch. Guilt, deep, deep guilt. Tinged with a need for revenge. It was as if a strange energy came out of it all. As if in burying it, it became possible to set it at a distance and look at it. I found myself writing him. I don't mean writing about him – I have never done that until now – but literally making him up out of what I knew. Extending him, imagining things he might say or do, or might have done or said. It was a kinetic, intuitive, loving kind of revenge. I wrote him into the film, of course. He was not its main character, all that had been decided, but he made a brilliant counterpoint. I'm sorry now that the way it came out was quite so stereotyped. I think that's to do with working with improvisation. The actor who played him was brilliant and he just got off on it all – the Midlands accent, the bit about being a butcher's apprentice, it was all a bit over the top but very hardcore, very neo-realist, quite authentic really. *The Independent* called the film: 'J.G. Ballard meets Ken Loach.'

I haven't been back to the house in years, but I think of it now as it was, say, on a late August evening: hot, the fields dry with chaff and stubble, the river a dark loop at the bottom of the field. In my mind's eye I watch the children as if in an old black and white film, their faces silently animated, laughing and talking, playing on the rope hanging from the tree by the river bank, their long wet hair swinging out as they jump from the rope into the river.

I live in Los Angeles now, in a real Californian house in Pasadena, with real mountains behind. I saw Neil recently, on a cable TV documentary, here in the States. He was talking about climbing in Yosemite and he seemed, you know, confident, tanned, easy, funny. Clearly he'd spent time in the US. And then I thought I saw him everywhere, I'd glimpse his walk, hear his face, catch sight of his hair – he has thick, curly brown hair – and my reaction was strange. I wanted to touch. I wanted to tell him it was OK now. In some confused way that I can't quite understand I wanted to say that I do know what it is I do. Stories. Shame, guilt, fear, love, regret, scuffs, stains, blood, signs of struggle. That's what I deal in now.

Roger Garfitt
The Horseman's Word
An extract from Part One

The farm where my father worked as a boy was Hill Farm,
Sedgeford. The village lies a few miles inland, in a dip behind
the chalk downs of the old coastline. Hill Farm, now part of a
large agricultural estate, lay to the left of the Heacham Road as it
climbs out of the village. The land began just below Sedgeford
church and ran up to Beech Wood at the top of the rise.

Hill Farm, Beech Wood: innocent names, that cannot
conceive of there being another beech wood, or another farm on
another hill. Names that belong to a time when travel was a rarity,
when roads were muddy sloughs and the world ended at the
parish boundary. Names that must have been repeated across
England, in parish after parish.

Hill Farm was owned by Mr Trenowath, a commanding figure
in breeches and brown leather gaiters. He had been a cavalryman
and from him my father learnt his love of horses. My first
memory of the farm is being taken into a stable to see one of the
Shires they were still using alongside the tractors. I was only
three or four and it towered over me, too big for my eyes to take
in. What I remember is the atmosphere of the stable: a stillness
I could almost touch, the gravity of that muscle and bone.

In the far corner of the yard was a dewpond, long dry but still
distinct, a shallow saucer of ground where the grass was greener.
My father told us how they used to lunge the horses there when
they were breaking them in. Over the years I heard him describe
it so often that in the end I saw him standing in the centre of the
dewpond, his hands spread like the hands of a clock. The minute
hand held the lunge line that ran from the heavy noseband. It

kept the line taut, moving with the horse as it trotted round the dewpond. The hour hand held the whip, pointed down so that its long lash trailed across the ground. Hour hand followed minute hand but the whip never gave more than a flick over the grass, like a horse's tail brushing away flies. The control was all in the voice. *Whoa!*, breathed in an undertone like a lullaby, calmed the animal down. A click of the tongue set it trotting again.

Once a horse had learnt its paces, the noseband was replaced by a bridle, a bit was slipped between its teeth, and it was walked on the long reins. This sounded risky: the first thing I was told about horses was to keep away from their back legs. But long reins were long: the trainer walked where the ploughman would be if the horse were pulling a plough. We had a photo of a horse coming out of the lane, its head up, pulling and resisting the turn. My father was behind it, a lad of sixteen or seventeen, slightly crouched, his back braced against the horse, his forearms taut, fingers flexing for control. He would walk a horse for miles, trying to keep his fingers supple; a light, fluent pressure on the reins, on the bit, on the soft mouth, even as his arms stiffened and his back ached.

On Show Saturdays in summer they would groom the horses at dawn, setting out for the showground through the early morning stillness and riding home in the last of the light. You only had to hear my father talk of those days to realize they were still part of him, more vivid than his own victories as a champion miler. His voice took on the hush of concentration, the allaying tones that would settle a stammer of hoofs and bring the horse back to a steady pace round the dewpond. What he recalled of his running was laying a trail for the harriers on the Boxing Day Hunt, to give everyone a good stretch at the start of the day.

He was one of three or four runners posted in the wood at the top of Eaton Farm, looking down on to the meet at Low Water. They had a haunch bone on the end of a rope and a bottle of aniseed. As soon as they saw the hounds move off, they splashed aniseed on to the bone and one of them would drag it across Eaton Farm to the bottom of Trenowath's Long Meadow. There they had built two jumps into the fence, the first of a series expressly designed to unseat the master, who was none too steady over jumps. They would haul the bone over, splash on some more aniseed and another runner would drag it to the next jump. It was a two-mile run and they only had a 400-yard start. By the time they reached Hill Farm, the hunt was on their heels. They had to be locked in a stable while the hounds cast around, yelping and sniffing for the lost scent.

Mr Trenowath had been like a second father to my father: and yet there was a distance, a deference that puzzled me when I was a child. My father would never drive straight into the farmyard. He parked the car in the lane and went to see if it was a good moment for us to call. Or he called on his own first and brought us later by arrangement. The lane opened into the yard, which looked homely enough. Ducks and geese grazed the short grass. Chickens roosted in an old hearse. The gate stood open. But there was an invisible line I never crossed without feeling I had to be on my best behaviour.

Now I realize my father was paying Mr Trenowath the respect that belonged to another time. Mr Trenowath was a farmer, my father a tradesman's son, a social distinction not even his entry into a learned profession could quite overcome. The formal call, the car parked in the lane, were bows to the village hierarchy as it had existed when my father was a child.

Nevertheless, he would have shown a similar courtesy if we had been calling on a smallholder. My father had tact that amounted to a sense of territory. Sharp as an animal instinct, he voiced it as human consideration. Visiting a strange farm, he would pause by the gate, looking and listening, judging whether it was a good moment to intrude. 'They're still milking,' he would say, 'we'll come back later.' In a garage or a builder's merchant he would glance around before he pressed the bell for service. If someone was clearly busy, he waited. He watched them move about their business with a kind of tenderness, as if he knew how intimate the rhythms of work were, how their mind would not rest until everything was back on the shelf and they were ready to attend to the next order.

This was all the more striking because my father is not, by nature, a patient man. Perhaps it came from knowing how much of my grandfather's personality was invested in the tools on his bench. Perhaps it came from his own need to be completed by rows of runner beans climbing their sticks, or a cyclamen growing from seed in a carefully tended pot in the greenhouse. For all the hours he spent in his study, my father was in abeyance there. He did not come alive until the gold-topped Parker was laid to rest on the pile of papers and he was outside in a pair of torn overalls, digging a trench for the potato clamp.

One summer, when I was still very young, we entered the farm from Beech Wood. I have no notion how we got there. Perhaps we caught the bus. Perhaps Grandad ran us out in the Maggot. All I remember is that we came into the corner of the field as they were cutting the last of the corn. Most of the field was bare, the sheaves already pitched on to the waggons. The tractor had stopped in front of a final small wedge of stalks. I looked up at the big wheel of the reaper, the red spokes that would cut the corn and sweep it into the binder. It was like looking up at a windmill, the triangular scoops of white canvas set like sails against the sky. I followed my father up the field. Something was happening. The men were coming down off the waggons. They were spacing out, forming a horseshoe round that last crest of corn. They made a gap and my father took his place in the line. One of them cocked a shotgun. My father reached down, I felt the touch of his hand on my chest: *Stay back!*

I was just outside the curve of the horseshoe. The tractor started up and I peered between the men's legs. A rabbit broke from the corn. It ran straight towards us, flat out, ears laid along its back. Came to the line of men and turned, only to find itself running into the curve. Tried to slew round, almost on its side now, skidding and scrambling for footholds in the dust. The men glanced along their line, like fielders signalling a catch. A black-haired man in a flat cap drew himself up and threw out his chest. As the rabbit ran in front of him, he fell forward. He came down on it like a plank.

He bounced back on to his feet, picked up his cap and tossed the rabbit behind him. The men roared, as for a brilliant catch, and he allowed himself a quiet smile. A fall so neat it might have been executed by a gymnast. That was what shocked me. One moment I had been watching an animal scrabbling to make a tight turn. I had glimpsed the white fur of its underbelly as its hind legs slipped in the dust. The next moment it had been hammered flat. The man drew himself up. He fell full length. His chest banged to the ground. I pictured it again, daring myself to look.

I could not repress my admiration. But there was something there I feared: that quiet smile, the man's pleasure in his deft blow. I might as well have feared the movement with which an Eskimo harpooned a seal. What I was seeing was a skill bred of hardship. There had been a series of agricultural depressions, the last of them ending only with the Second World War. For decades the only meat a labourer and his family ate was bacon on a Sunday, from the pig they kept in the back garden. The rest of the week he took bread and onion to the field, with a smear of bacon fat. The woods and fields abounded with game but the gentry owned everything that ran or flew or swam. Poachers snared and lamped at night and sold their catch in the pubs. Otherwise farm labourers learnt to keep their eyes open, to dive on a hare if they passed one crouched in a field, to drop on a rabbit if it ran under their feet. When I think of that smile now, I feel he had a right to it. He had learnt that trick in a hard world.

Rabbits were a plague until another plague was inflicted on them: myxomatosis. Every cornfield was thinned and pitted at the edge. They flattened corners quicker than a thunderstorm. I heard of whole fields eaten down to a few wisps. Cutting the last of the corn was a chance to even the odds. Whatever had retreated deeper into the corn when the reaper first circled the field was trapped there. Foxes, hares, rabbits, rats all huddled together in the remaining stalks. Half the village turned out to watch or to take their place in the line.

Every year my father borrowed a shotgun from Mr Trenowath. One morning, looking over our teacups and seeing an empty pillow on the double bed, we would be told he had gone shooting. This sudden absence was tantalizing. Imagine rising in the dark and slipping out of the house while everyone else slept . . . I woke to find I had missed an adventure.

By mid-morning he had returned with a shoulderbag full of rabbits. Once he brought home a mallard drake, a strange creature, completely of water, its green neck shimmering like the surface of a pond. The sun was out and a gold light seemed to float over it. The sun went in and it turned to a cold silver. The sleek keel, we discovered, was all waterproofing, a tight thatch of feathers, inches thick. It was like trying to pluck velvet, our fingers ached as the layers diminished to a fine, stubborn down.

I watched my father skinning and gutting rabbits so often that, years later, I found I could do it from memory. By now I had recovered from my shock. I was only too anxious to be taken shooting. 'When you're older,' I was told; the inevitable reply. I had heard it so often I had lost any sense of its meaning.

To my surprise, when I was ten, my father decided I was old enough. I could walk behind with the game bag, as long as I was careful to keep behind. The next morning he woke me at four, one of those hours I'd always imagined must be like outer space. They were habitable, it seemed. There was oxygen, though perhaps not quite enough. I felt a little dizzy: still prickling from the numbness of sleep.

The sky was just beginning to lighten as we drove towards Sedgeford. The dark bulk of Beech Wood rose on our right.

'There's the gateway!' My father drove straight on.

'Someone's just gone through the gate on the other side. I think it's the gamekeeper from the estate.'

'But we've got permission from Mr Trenowath.'

'Yes, but the keeper doesn't know us. If he sees us parking, he'll only worry what we're up to. Much better to wait a few minutes and let him go peacefully on his rounds.'

My father's tact. We drove down into Sedgeford and sat for ten minutes outside Grandad's shop.

By the time we returned to Beech Wood, the sky was a thunderhead blue, with black hanging in heavy streaks like rain. There was a thin grey light under the trees. We seemed to be moving through a primitive world, only half evolved. I searched the tangle of treetops for the silhouettes of pigeons. I thought I saw one and my father aimed into the primeval light. Before he could fire, a pigeon clattered down from a lower branch and sank into the grey.

We came out of the wood into daylight, the grass shining between long patches of shadow. My father advanced into the meadow and I kept a careful six paces behind. We were walking so slowly a rabbit sat up to watch. I should have said, 'Over to your left!', but now I was hesitant, afraid to break my father's concentration. By the time I spoke, the rabbit was running along the edge of the field. My father fired after it into the hedge.

Then our luck turned. Rabbits in a patch of sunlight. As they scattered, my father fired and the shot rolled one right over. We repeated this in the next field, and the next. The game bag filled and the strap began to pull under my shoulder. I carried it uncomplaining, too proud to fidget under the weight. That ache was my investiture.

We came out on to the slope of a cornfield they had cut the day before. Bales glinted across the stubble's white haze. The reaper and binder had just been replaced by a combine and these building blocks of straw were new to me. There were small stacks of them, fours and sixes, along the slope above us. As we started downhill, I heard a faint drumming like an echo in the ground. Something was running on the slope. My father turned and fired between the stacks. He had seen a flash of yellow fur, the size of a fox.

It was a hare, so big we had to lift it by the feet and carry it between us. The body hung down, long and heavy and rank. The men looked up in surprise as we entered the farmyard. They gathered around us. They held the hare up by the hind legs and measured its length. They passed it to each other and weighed it in their hands. Later, in the kitchen, Grandma would grumble that it was a doe in kindle. The meat would be scraggy, she said, hardly worth the trouble. But for that moment nothing soured our triumph. We felt like two hunters home from the hill, the carcass of a deer slung between us.

That morning was the only time I saw the inside of the farmhouse, which was set back on a terrace of lawn above a low stone wall, just where the lane broadened out into the yard. The sun was hot and we had been in the fields since dawn. Mr Trenowath invited us in and immediately I felt my father's eye upon me. As we went through the gate, his whole body seemed to stoop over me, saying, *Best behaviour now!* The house itself, a long frontage of weathered brick with tall casement windows, had a robust dignity. The terrace gave it an added reserve, a gentlemanly detachment that seemed to match Mr Trenowath's own.

Two or three low stone steps took us on to the terrace, an ascent so gradual I hardly noticed it in the drowse of sunlight. The door opened into a flagstoned hall, cool and whitewashed. A lance hung on the far wall, over saddles and harness. The floor was the colour of history. It was like entering a castle and finding it still garrisoned: a washstand in the corner, a kitchen table against one wall, almost hidden by a wooden screen.

I walked in the echo of the men's footsteps as they crossed the hall and turned into the sitting room. I saw the fireplace and remembered my father telling me how, in the days before Mabel came as housekeeper, he would cook a rabbit in a bucket over the open fire, making a rough stew with swedes and turnips.

Now we were in a gentler epoch. Mabel appeared from her kitchen at the other end of the house and Mr Trenowath asked her to make some coffee, and bring a glass of lemonade for me. I perched myself in the window seat and fixed my gaze on the hall, on the stones' armoured gleam that seemed to stretch back seven or eight hundred years.

As we stood in the doorway, saying goodbye, sunlight slanted in, warming and softening the flagstones. Mr Trenowath was at his ease, framed in the door with the saddles on the wall behind him, the bridles looped on their pegs. A pair of riding boots stood to attention against the wainscot, braced by their trees to a stiff shine. He was smiling, for a moment almost like an uncle or a grandfather, looking down at me out of a life in which he was clearly content. But when I caught sight of the washstand, tucked into its corner below the saddles, I felt a chill under the sunlight. For the first time in my life, I had witnessed solitude.

When I thought of Trenowath's after that, I found that my memories of the place had changed. The farm had become an interior, a silence. I could taste it on my tongue, as cold and clear as spring water. Nothing could have been plainer or more distinct from everything I knew. This made me thoughtful. Until then Norfolk had been mine for the imagining, a world of differences where I could never be a stranger. I had moved in and out of my grandparents' lives, absorbing them into mine. Elusive as the past was, that other country I glimpsed in the front-room photographs, my own studio portrait stood on the piano, a small boy with crinkly ears and a toothy smile, his cheeks tinted an embarrassing shade of pink by the photographer, that gave me right of entry. Now I began to wonder how far I had really seen into these lives that so intrigued me. There was no absorbing the silence of Trenowath's, no diminishing its strangeness.

Years later, watching the film of *Far From the Madding Crowd*, I saw the farm again. Mr Boldwood was sitting alone at a mahogany table, eating a meal prepared by his housekeeper. Bare flagstones resonated with the tock of a carriage clock. It was the same atmosphere as Trenowath's: austerity and high polish, the solitude of a kept house – and Bathsheba's Valentine bewitching him from the mantelpiece.

The Pickets
for Terence Brown

Blockade

Where ideology fails, mere livelihood
takes over, seeking its bottom line,
wherever that is, in vision or in blood

or further regions impossible to define.
The cross of St George flutters on the pole
behind men picketing in a benign

huddle, comfy, but barely in control
of the world that they are bringing into being.
They form a solid yeomanry in droll

revolt against powers that even now are fleeing
the cities they rule from. From what far regions
have the yeomen risen? Where are their all-seeing

leaders and prophets? Their everyday religions
are bottom-line affairs with few demands,
offering basic warmth for mild allegiance,

Poetry

composed of mostly affordable deodands:
crumbs for the ducks, a tip for the paperboy,
a Christmas kiss, holding a mother's hands,

comfort for the dying. I'm thinking of Joy,
Ruby, Ted and Jerry, their children trapped in
kitchens and sheds a real storm would destroy

in minutes, and Stan, hollow eyed, flat capped,
whose tools we inherited, and Percy Bunn
the handyman and glazier who dropped

dead at the church fête, and gangling Ron
the caretaker, whose wife left and he drank
for weeks, and every picket the son

(or daughter) of people of such social rank
as drop away now, lost in the dawn retreat,
the tankers rolling past them, faces blank.

Orators

The orators came, voting with their feet
and shows of hands. Hands were grasping fags,
clutching and pounding. I remember the discreet

look of the cabinet minister and the bags
under Ron Kosky's eyes as he talked of Paul
Robeson and of the black slaves in their rags.

Thick eyebrows were watching punched cards fall
on office desks. So Gerry Sparks would follow
Frank Chappell to the mighty annual

TUC where Jack Jones laid down the law
('Get your tanks off my lawn,' said Callaghan)
while Red Robbo at BL tunnelled away below,

and I was scared of everything: the man
with the power to turn lights off and drop
me back into the chaos where I began

among mobs and bodies, the horde's gallop
towards a single figure which was me
by extension. This was England's shop

with windows broken and nothing inside to see,
and England's work as represented by
estate kids, blokes on buses, Bill and Tubby

in the painter's yard. I would not say
it was a sheltered childhood, but the loud
disturbed me, as did anger and decay.

I was a spectator, watching the crowd
wearing the faces of furious angels: their roar
was me in flames. Soon enough they slowed

back to the daily trudge, the regular shore,
their sea slapping and ebbing, their kind
gestures returning with them to the shop floor

and the parlour and the pub, fags in lined
hands, jokes and telly, the world unaltered,
as if like me, it feared to be defined.

Orgreave

Out of the dark came the miners. Their villages
were live coals and their bodies fed the flames
that burnt their love affairs and marriages.

Black dust coated their tongues and blurred their dreams.
They licked their children into shape like bears
with sore heads. At night they heard the screams

of wheels on tracks or footsteps on the stairs.
They'd rise to the surface and gradually fade
into the morning. They covered their chairs

with rough shadows that left a faint grey tide.
They drank hard and played football with caps for goalposts,
a few turned out for a professional side

in the nearby town. They prayed for the Lord of Hosts
to lead them into a world of light but woke
at midnight hearing their brothers' ghosts.

Wheels on tracks, collapses. They only needed to poke
the fire for the coals to cave in and bury them deep.
I still remember the day their power broke

at Ollerton, Bidworth, Orgreave. The earth could keep
its darkness. It was the end of the century right now,
the end of the war. A new kind of peace would creep

out of the atom with pale hands, its brow
unlined and vacant. There was something deadly
about its frivolity, which would allow

anything at all except fire and memory.

Scene at a Conference

The Kindliness of the English: a paper presented
to the ethnicity conference in Dublin in
2004. The thesis commented

on their slow smiles in a suburban garden
in North London in the early 1960s. It cited
a middle-aged hand fingering a pattern

of glossy box-hedge leaves. On being invited
to elaborate, the writer mentioned the old
woman who shyly brought cups of tea to benighted

refugees waiting for a bus one particularly cold
December; three boys in a playground taking
pity on a loner in the doorway who would unfold

an incomprehensible story to them, shaking
with tears; WVS squadrons, patient
bureaucrats at office desks, their heads aching

with figures, and surprisingly efficient
bands of secretaries holding open lines,
all comprehending, almost omniscient.

The constancy of kindliness. The signs
of kindliness on rain-soaked building sites,
electric substations and down coal mines.

The forms of kindliness: terrible nights
of diffidence in front rooms, quiet
interminable minutes interrupted by flights

of fancy, the unspoken etiquette
of the lower-middle-class tea party – loss
and the coping with – desire within set

Poetry

limits: all this equated with kindliness.
Warm beer and cricket, mumbled someone
at the back, who had already given his address.

And it was true, there was considerably more fun
at the Gael end of things, at the high table:
charm, invention, a recently fired gun.

Nostalgia

I recall the 1970s sliding underfoot
like dead wet leaves. It was perpetual
late history nibbling at the root

of a gaudy tree. The summer had been lethal.
So many dead and there was no escape
except down cellars. It was the long crawl

to seeming safety that did for us. We lost shape,
shrank back into ourselves, turned minimalist,
steely trimmers, each with a secret tape

of fear. Russia showed us a clenched fist.
Their guns were pointing as were everyone's.
The world was tired. It would not be missed

by bodies in car boots, fingers pressing buttons.
I don't think we were doing retro then
but who can tell? Shirley had bought patterns

from a stall on the Friday market. There were women
rummaging among hats, cheap scarves and rolls
of cotton, Terylene and other off-cuts. When

did this stop, if it has? And those armfuls
of Mills and Boon in the corner? When did they
switch to Black Lace, dream catchers and lentils?

Some decades age faster than others. We replay
them like old movies. The pickets flying high
over a ruined industrial estate have flown away

into the grey cancer-ridden darkness to die.
And these men are like a flock of starlings
briefly gathered by the refinery

now risen and gone with a lazy flap of wings.

Jose Luis Padrón Plazaola Poetry

Translated by Amaia Gabantxo

Introduction by Amaia Gabantxo

Jose Luis Padrón Plazaola, born in 1970, is one of the new generation of Basque poets. He's a script-writer, a translator, and a literature critic and art critic. He's also a bilingual poet who writes in both Basque and Spanish. Since his first collection of poetry, *Ilargirik gabeko kalea* (*The Street Without a Moon*), was awarded the Urruzuno Prize in 1987, he has collected every other available poetry prize in the Basque country.

The poems published here are from his award-winning collection of love poetry, *Ibaia euri erasotan bezala* (*Like a River under the Tempest*), which won the Basque Academy of Letters Prize 1998 and which I am currently translating.

Basque is a minority language: only a few people living between the north of Spain and the south of France speak it. A very complex language, it is thought by some to be the oldest in Europe. It is very rich in vocabulary and, because of its agglutinating nature (prepositions, adverbs and articles 'hook' onto the end of nouns and verbs to make compounds), it's particularly suited to the purposes of poetry-making. This doesn't necessarily mean that there are more poets in the Basque country than in other places in the world: in fact, if news items are to be believed, the only poetry coming from the Basque country is that arising in a swirling, smoky flourish from the stout end of a .33 millimetre Parabellum.

How did I ever come to learn the name of that gun? Curiously, by means of a poetic device: repetition.

Poetry

But of course there is poetry in the Basque country. It could even be argued that societies in the midst of violent conflict are a particularly fertile seedbed for beautiful poetry. Flowers in the dirt. Think Heaney, think Muldoon, think McGuckian. C'est la vie.

And so, yes, Padrón Plazaola is an astonishing poet, and his poetry must reach the ears of those who want to listen – particularly if it's translated. From Basque into English. From the language of a minority living in chaos to the language of globalization, the internet and CNN. Not that I can imagine anyone reading one of Padrón Plazaola's poems on international TV, but it is a comforting thought to know they're there if ever anyone feels like doing so. Instead of the bombs and the close-range shots in the head, please.

Like a River under the Tempest is a collection of love poetry. These poems hurt. Love in the midst of conflict is never easy; how can you love when . . . ? But it's not necessary to finish that sentence. Just read the poems, they'll speak to you too.

Translated text

I Offer You Everything

I offer you everything,
give you all.
Strengths and weaknesses,
this pilgrimage of
winters and fires.

I offer you everything,
give you all.
The birds, the distant
rivers and nearby skies,
every morning.

I offer you everything,
give you all.
Stars and rhymes,
a lonely spirit as it darkens,
variations of the soul.

I offer you everything,
give you all.
My desire, my will.
I am you for you,
for you I will be you,
undone, an empty husk.

A Kiss

Your dark
pained eyes found me out
immediately,
as if I'd forgotten to present you with a dress
or were to bare your body's beauty and but behold it
as if they'd been sown
without hope of harvest.

Our Happiness

Our happiness
needs so little.
Birds ruffled by the wind,
aphrodite and hades at play,
the life of a single day,
a communion of hearts,
huddled-silent forests of light,
unpredictable monotony
and the moon watching us.

Georg Trakl Poetry

Translated by Will Stone

Introduction by Will Stone

'He perished beneath the unbearable weight of his own existence' said Rilke of Trakl, after the latter's sudden death from an overdose of cocaine in 1914. Though Trakl was only twenty-seven when he died, within a short space of time (1910-1914), he, like Rimbaud before him, managed to reveal to an almost supernatural degree his intense inner struggle. He left behind an extraordinary body of poems which all but convince the reader of the validity of indulging in a fanatical heroism of the imagination when faced with the wretchedness of reality. In these translations I have attempted to bring Trakl through the maelstrom of language exchange in as reasonable shape as possible. My fundamental aim is to give an English language reader the poetry of Trakl, not just to render a direct English equivalent of the language he used. One must be humble and faithful, but one must also be creative in a poetic sense and take risks if the new language is to support the essence of a poet who can truly be said to have drowned in the dark wake of his art.

Poetry

Translated text

Dream of Evil

A gong's sound, golden brown, dying out –
A lover wakes in black chambers
Cheek to stars that flicker at the window.
On the river, rope, mast and sail blaze.

A monk, a pregnant woman in the crowd.
Guitars that strum, the shimmer of scarlet frocks.
Sultry, in golden gleams the chestnuts wither away;
Black looms the church's dismal panoply.

From pale masks peers the spirit of evil.
A square darkens, morbid and terrible;
Whispers well up on the islands at nightfall.

Lepers who may rot away at night
Read confused omens from the birdflight.
Brother and sister spy on each other
Trembling in the park.

The Wayfarer

Ever the white night leans against the hill,
Where in silver sound the poplar looms,
Star and stone can be found.

Sleeping, the path arches over the torrent,
A dead face follows the boy,
Crescent moon in the rosy ravine.

Shepherds praising far off. In old rocks
The toads gaze out with crystal eyes,
The blossoming wind awakes, the bird voice
Of one as dead,
And steps green softly in the wood.

These recall tree and beast, slow steps
And the moon,   (of moss;
That glowing sinks into mournful waters.

He turns back and strolls to the green strand,
Rocking on black gondolas through the
Decayed city.

The Horror

I saw myself passing through abandoned rooms.
The stars danced demented on a blue background
And lonely howled the dogs in the fields.
Madly heaved the wind in the tops of trees.

But suddenly: stillness! A dull fever glow
Commands venomous flowers to bloom from my mouth
And from the branches dew falls as from a wound
Pale, shimmering, and falls; and falls like blood.

Out of the treacherous vacancy of a mirror
A face rises slowly and imprecisely
Out of horror and darkness: Cain!

So softly whispers the velvet curtain.
Through the window the moon gazes out
As into emptiness.
There I am alone with my murderer.

Dejection

Through afternoon the spectre of world calamity.
Huts flee through little gardens brown and forlorn.
Guttering light hovers around burnt manure,
Two sleepers sway homewards, grey and obscure.

On the withered grass a child runs
And plays, with his eyes black and smooth.
Gold drips from bushes dreary and bleak,
An old man turns sadly in the wind.

At nightfall once more above my head
Saturn mutely steers a wretched fate.
A tree, a dog steps back behind itself
And black reels God's heaven and defoliates.

A little fish glides quickly down the stream;
And softly stirs the dead friend's hand
And lovingly smoothes brow and garment.
A light bids shadows in the rooms awake.

Night

I sing you wild fissure,
In the night storm
Soaring mountains;
You grey towers
Spilling with hellish grimaces,
Animals aflame,
Harsh ferns, spruces,
Crystal flowers.
Agony everlasting,
That you hunt for God,
Tender spirit,
Sighing in the falls,
Among the surging pines.

Golden flares the fire
About the gathered peoples.
Above blackish outcrops
Drunk with death
Plunges the glowing-wind bride,
The blue surge
Of the glacier
And powerfully sounds the bell
In the valley:
Flames, curses
And the dark play of lust,
A hardened head
Storms heaven.

Raoul Schrott
Poetry
Translated by Iain Galbraith

A History of the Written Language IV

the streak of the fulgurite · a limonite
and its spheres · the cross of the
hæmatite in drifted sand under the
red lines of the gneiss: ciphers and
their bodies · the tendon tautening at
your armpit and the tuft of hair like
tamarisk needles the wind has
scattered blue and black: all these
signs and forms · the mouth pressed
to a stone speaking them into the
void · an alphabet without vowels
circles lines and dots etched in the
rock · the engraving of arbitrary
contours and two triangles tip to tip
between these the outline of a
woman and the handful of water that
brings the colours back to life · it is
cool under this overhanging rock in
this cave of the sun · that is the land
and what was once a river · the first
letter the flight of cranes to the south
their narrow V pointing to the sky

wadi tshuinat, 13.01.96

A History of the Written Language VI

the wind before dawn is a missive
from north-west erring against the
night · i write these lines to you
from a house of salt · etesian tiles
crumbling into the lake · that is how
i build with words · as if you were
here the brown blanket on the bed
casting its folds over your sleep
your shoulders · you sit up and go
to the door · water runs through the
ditches under the palms and the
stalks of bushes and the moon
writes a comma in a pool its sickle
scratched to the enamel and
blackened like a pot on the fire
before it your back and a line of
light rising to your knee · the loose
strap of your sandal dragging in the
sand was like a quill always poised
to write a letter · and then again

gabroon, 08.01.96

Albert Einstein: General Relativity

it was predicted that a solar eclipse would take place
     on 29 may 1919 · two expeditions

were launched and equipped at some expense
     with artificial horizons tripods lenses and emulsions

one sent to principe off the west african coast
     the other to sobral in brazil to trace

the same event · in his room eddington watched the door post
    gnawed to dust by termites saw clouds too dense

to dissipate or drain · crommelin found the jungle
    silent but heard the insects hissing

from his packet · on principe the governor's
    villa consisted mainly of bottles and books

in the brazilian village they started pissing
    blood their hands raw with fist-sized sores

on the atlantic island that belonged to portugal
    was an empty church and on a hook

in the tower stairwell a purple robe but nightly in sobral
footsteps echoed in the trampled alley

between the huts · eddington's instruments
    succumbed to the sultry heat his wolfram metal

threatened by rust · crommelin sent two documents
    but the package ended up in cabo verde

the day appointed on the island of principe brought
    bad weather · yet the sun's fine penumbra

was plainly visible in sobral the silver ions on the plate
revealing near its edge a bright spot

that delivered proof the light of a star
    was deflected by the sun's dark deadweight

oxford, 06.11.1919

Lines – Gregg Potter <tupper61@hotmail.com>

Sarah May
Somewhere in the Middle of Nowhere

I had been in Macedonia for three months when my left ear stopped working. Living in a foreign country is one thing; being ill in a foreign country is another. In a certain amount of panic and considerable amount of pain, we phoned our Albanian translator, Ilyriana, whose husband was a medical student. Within an hour they were sat in the back of our car giving us directions to their local clinic. All I remember of the clinic is pink walls and women in white overalls. I got it into my head that they looked like Eastern European spa attendants. I've never been to an Eastern European spa and have therefore never laid eyes on the sort of attendants who might or might not work there, but this is what I was convinced they looked like.

We were seen immediately. I don't know what Ilyriana said to the clinic staff; whether we were given preferential treatment or not. Maybe it was a quiet night. In any event, I was beyond caring. By the time I sat down in the green Formica chair in one of the consulting rooms, no sounds from the outside world were making their way into my left ear. The only thing I could hear was the thudding of my blood vessels. A sound which, despite signifying life, quickly becomes monotonous.

One of the spa attendants did some mildly unobtrusive things I've never had done before, such as placing a wooden spatula on my tongue and sticking tweezers up my nostrils. After this she diagnosed infection and claimed there was nothing she could do. I gave two hundred dinars to someone behind a pane of frosted glass and we left, heading back into the cold Skopje night towards the General Hospital at the foot of Vodna, a mountain we could see from our apartment.

Somewhere in the Middle of Nowhere

I hate hospitals in the same way I hate being ill. Skopje General looked as though it had been through a war. The walls were caramel brown and sustaining the sort of injuries you could only put down to severe structural damage. Although the hospital was meant to be full to capacity, it felt and sounded empty. There was no furniture, institutionalized or other, apart from a green bench on the second floor occupied by a man in pyjamas, who was smoking and staring into space. The scene was strangely domestic; he looked more like the victim of some recent marital disharmony than a patient. Most of the panes of glass in the stairwell were broken, creating a freeway for the moths which covered the walls. I followed Ilyriana and her husband blindly.

Only the week before, her husband had failed his medical exams. I don't know whether there were academic grounds for his failing, but Ilyriana had informed me with confidence that he would pass next time round. For a small sum of Deutsche Marks. Was this what is known as corruption? For a split second I wanted to know, intensely, the truth of the matter. Then I stopped caring.

We reached a corridor not quite as desolate as the others. A patient emerged from a windowless room where there was a green screen, a desk, spotlight, swivel chair and two ferociously fashionable female doctors. Even the white coats looked like accessories. Ilyriana's husband started speaking and, whatever he was saying, he was saying it with pride. The two women looked unimpressed, suspicious even, barely twitching their heavily painted lips as he spoke. However, within minutes I was sat in the consultation chair, the left-hand side of my face on fire because of the close proximity of the large spotlight. A reassuring nod from Ilyriana. They were not only going to see me at the end of their shift, but free of charge.

Another wooden spatula was produced, as well as the nostril tweezers. Followed swiftly by the emergence of an ambitiously large, aptly named Alexander syringe. There was an infection in my ear, she announced, but this was due to an obstruction. She wielded the Alexander syringe a couple of times, while her colleague half-heartedly inspected my not very impressive assemblage of clothing. The obstruction wouldn't move and I remained deaf to the outside world in one ear. It was the end of their shift; they'd tried.

It was verging on eleven p.m. There was another hospital, Ilyriana tirelessly informed us: a military one. There was a doctor there her husband knew. If he was working, maybe we could get seen. The military hospital wasn't so desolate. Like the General, there was no sign of any patients but there were doctors. We walked, unchallenged, up and down miles of corridor. Ilyriana's husband spoke to some of the doctors we passed but there was nobody either able or willing to wield an Alexander syringe and give me back my hearing. But then, why should there have been?

The evening was taking a hallucinogenic turn and I was slipping into a state of panic. I needed to be fully-functioning in order to exist here, in a world beyond my mother tongue. I appreciated Ilyriana's husband's relentlessness, which in the end outlived my own. As a last resort we tried a private German clinic but it was closed. In agony and overwhelmed by the sound of my own heartbeat, which was all I could hear in my left ear, we gave in for the night.

The next morning, after a phone call to a friend at the American Embassy, I managed to get to see the nurse there. She didn't have an Alexander syringe and we ended up having to improvise with smaller syringes whose hypodermic needles needed removing first. It was no good. As a compromise she gave me some antibiotics for the infection. These came from a voluptuous glass-fronted cabinet, and I got the impression from her slight hesitation before opening it that this cabinet was the envy of most medical practitioners in the city. She also phoned the secretary of somebody she referred to with reverence as Doctor Sophia, an ear, nose and throat specialist who taught at the university, but happened that very day to have a clinic at the General.

It took our small entourage which consisted of my friend, the nurse and myself, at least twenty minutes to leave the Embassy compound. I had forgotten that it was a year to the day since the bombing of Belgrade began and protesters had attacked the Embassy. My friend had barely been able to get to her desk that morning for US snipers, and before they opened the gates for us security personnel with white bomb detectors disappeared underneath the car we were in.

We arrived at the hospital and the nurse led us to a different, more populated part than the night before. My entourage gave the misleading impression that I was somebody important. As a consequence we accomplished an embarrassing queue jump – over a queue of people suffering, I presume, the same sort of pain as me.

The fact that Dr Sophia looked like an Italian porn star seemed to strike nobody but me. There must have been, however, some traces of this emotion in my face because the nurse from the Embassy chose that moment to remind me of Dr Sophia's credentials. I was taken to an examination room where I lay on a couch and listened to the rattling arrival of a tin of instruments. Had I seen rust on them? These instruments were pushed into my inflamed ear by Dr Sophia's experienced hands; Dr Sophia was not squeamish about causing pain. I dredged up from somewhere my old dentist's instruction that if I raised my right arm to indicate pain, then he would stop drilling. My raised right arm, however, was knocked to one side and I was scolded like a child. They thought I was a child.

Dr Sophia explained that the obstacle in my ear was attached to the drum and that her prodding was an attempt to prise it away. I held on to my gut, giving full vent to fear instead, a fear that I would be rendered deaf here, of all places. But then hadn't this, deep down, been my fear all along? Not of being rendered deaf here but, worse than that, of dying here? In the middle of nowhere? Because dying in the middle of nowhere would render my death meaningless, and a meaningless death would be even worse than a meaningless life.

At last Dr Sophia gave up her relentless prodding. Unable, despite my importance, to conceal her frustration at my intolerably low pain threshold, she handed me over to the elderly nurse I had seen on arrival wielding her Alexander syringe. Once again I was in the large communal clinic with no screens and a serpent's tail of a queue.

One nurse held my hair back, while the older expert directed high-pressure jets of warm water into my ear canal. In front of everyone. The lack of privacy enabled me to attain new heights of hysteria. The old nurse with over fifty years of experience was unable to remove the obstruction. Dr Sophia reappeared in order to charge me the foreigner's treatment rate. Having never paid for medical treatment in my life before, I had crossed her threshold empty handed and was unable to produce the requisite number of Deutsche Mark. She charged it to the Embassy instead, under the illusion created by my earlier arrival with accompanying entourage.

I had spent the last forty-eight hours scouring Skopje in search of a cure I had known all along I probably wouldn't find. But then any action is better than inaction. It struck me suddenly that a lot of the people we had met through my husband's work with an NGO based in Skopje were doing exactly the same thing. An extraordinary amount of good work was being done in Macedonia, against all odds, by those who had been working in the camps since the Kosova crisis when the country was flooded by over a quarter of a million refugees. There was also a lot of bad work being done, which had its roots in the remnants of a colonial or missionary mentality. But what if this misplaced combination of charity and goodwill, with its own peculiarly persistent form of arrogance, concealed something far more simple? What if it concealed nothing more than envy? If one aid worker I met who urged us to leave a mess on her floor in order to give the cleaner something to do was ever able to admit this to herself, what else might she not admit? That she hadn't come to cure but to be cured? How dare they have a war without her?

I had thought that only bribery and corruption lay between my ear and the potential cure of the Alexander syringe. Actually what lay between them was the Ottoman Empire, the collapse of the Ottoman Empire, the Balkan Wars, two World Wars, over four decades of Socialist rule, the emergence of a new Republic. I had forgotten all this; but these people – and Dr Sophia, the man in his pyjamas in the hospital the other night and of course the nurse wielding the Alexander syringe – they hadn't forgotten.

History, as I was taught, is linear. A march forward, and each step forward, a step for civilization. Here, history was concentric. You didn't have to look backwards, only to either side of you. Here, somewhere in the middle of nowhere, history was being made and will continue to be made. Isn't this why we came? Like many other things, history is something we don't make any more. Ours is a culture of forgetting, which is why we're so obsessed with anniversaries, ceremonies . . . remembering. How can you remember something you've never forgotten?

Dr Sophia offered to take me home. Was this kindness on her part or a continuation of the illusion that I was somebody important? Why did this matter to me anyway when I was in pain still, and getting an unexpected lift home? What did I want? The truth again? We went into the staff room where she chatted with another doctor about a patient who had been sent to Germany for an operation. She undressed in front of me, changing into her civilian clothes while apologizing for the lack of facilities at the hospital. I didn't know why I was standing in that room in the middle of a foreign city watching a strange woman undress. I was burning to ask her a question I was convinced she knew the answer to, but I didn't know what the question was.

We left the hospital. Her husband was waiting for her in a car outside. He didn't like me; I saw it immediately. Was this something his wife did a lot, and that he disapproved of? Picking up foreigners? I sat in the back of the car next to their son and talked with Dr Sophia about nursery care, organized to clearly superior levels of logic. She invited my family skiing. When I made no reply, she volunteered the information that she had been to a reception at the American Ambassador's residence. There was that question on the tip of my tongue again. What did I want to say? We parted ways.

We never went skiing with Dr Sophia and her family. I know now that Dr Sophia is Bulgarian. She is a nose, throat and ear specialist. She has a husband who is a psychologist and a four-year-old son who likes nursery. On Fridays she has a clinic at the General hospital, and the rest of the time she works at the university. She may or may not have once attended a reception at the American Ambassador's residence. What does she know about me? That I'm the wife of a high-ranking diplomat? Hardly. Yet I never once attempted to correct her and I never paid my bill.

My ear cured itself without further medical intervention.

Mehmet Yashim
Fifth Tale: You've Been Called Up
Translated by Ümit Hussein

A small Turkish flag hung from the front of the bicycle. The bottoms of her trouser legs kept dragging along the ground and tripping her up. Her sandals made odd clattering sounds. While she was trying to undo her hairslide, a group of long-haired university students in jeans, back on the island for the summer holidays, passed her.

Most of them were carrying Stens.

'Stens remind me of school more than war. You had to get at least five out of ten in warcraft. Firing at school was fun. War . . . History books explain it away in two sentences. Will all our experiences be squeezed into one little sentence in a book too? Won't any book write the history of the young boy with the Sten propped up on his shoulder? Won't they say what was going through his head at that moment?

The warlike atmosphere was completed by the military marches on the radio. The doors and windows of the houses were closed. The only sounds to be heard in the streets were military marches and gunfire.

The streets are like something out of an American movie called: *The Town that Lost its Voice!*

Someone was whistling behind her. The girl glanced back furtively. When she saw it was Erol she stopped.

'How are things? There isn't any trouble where you are, is there?' she asked.

Erol forced a smile, showing his teeth. 'No. Things are fine,' he said and, 'I'm being called up.'

And he smiled again.

'You as well?'

'I don't know for sure but they'll probably send for me in about a week.'

'They called up the boys in our area too. Even the fifteen-year-olds went,' she told him.

The girl ran her fingers through her long brown hair. She tried to put it up. She held the hairslide she'd taken out of her pocket between her teeth. They chatted away about anything and everything that wasn't the war. As Elvis's Place was open, they went in and bought ice cream. Sitting there, eating ice cream, it was easy to pretend that there wasn't a war on at all.

His hair was long. He hadn't long been shaving. He was wearing a Pink Floyd T-shirt. He looked at his watch while he rang the bell. It was nearly four. Ömer opened the door. He was wearing shorts and was still half asleep. Erol could still taste ice cream in his mouth.

'Good job you came. I'm bored stiff,' Ömer said.

The long-haired boy stared at him vacantly. He didn't know whether he was bored or not. While Ömer was getting dressed they talked about where new fighting had broken out that day, which areas had been bombed and how many people they knew from the latest list of war prisoners.

They went out. They walked in silence. Walking in silence bored Ömer. His boredom seared through the silence.

'Say something, will you? Your face is the most miserable . . .'

'Zafer's been called up too,' Erol said.

'One by one, two by two, we're all going to the war. Before I could have told you what the war was. From what I learned from my father, from my teacher and from books and television. But I can't any more. I realized that when war broke out. I used to be able to tell you anything you wanted to know about it. I learned in history, in warcraft, in first aid, in the plays they put on on national holidays . . . I don't know anything any more.'

Zafer was at home listening to tapes when they arrived. He started to tell them what had happened as soon as they walked in, gesturing wildly with his hands and arms.

'Atteeeen-shun! You wait till I get my A-4 . . . I'll be standing behind that recoilless going Bang bang bang!'

Zafer's mother came into the room carrying a tray of iced lemonade. She was short and wore her hair up in a bun, which made her look like an aged child.

'Haven't you been called up yet?' she asked.

Adding a false smile to their permanent expression of bewilderment and boredom, they looked at her and said, 'No.'

She indicated Zafer and shook her head. 'I told him to pretend he was younger. Everyone lies about their age and gives false addresses but this fool wants to make out he's a hero.'

'What about Mustafa? He was younger than me and he didn't even wait to be called up before he went.'

'Well then, you can go and die with him.'

Zafer's mother seemed more angry than worried. It was as though someone had told her to her face that her son wasn't as good as other boys and she had taken it as a personal insult. It wasn't like her son was the only lamb available for sacrifice; everyone should be in the same position. She turned to the others.

'You'll be called up one of these days too, you'll see!' She said and left the room, muttering to herself.

Zafer had turned pale. His green eyes were popping out of his head. Like a frog. Actually, no, they were human eyes that showed what he really felt inside.

'My uncle said there was nothing to worry about. He said that all your fears and worries disappear once you get a gun in your hand.'

'I'm going to come home with a Takarof. And I'm going to have missiles and hand grenades in my bag . . .'

'I won't die, it's only cowards that die . . .'

Erol played the guitar when he got home. Then he got fed up. He listened to the records he had taped from the charts. Then he got fed up. He changed all the posters in his room around. Then he got fed up again. He had dreams for the future. Great dreams that it would be too embarrassing to tell anyone else about. Of that girl's long black hair, for instance . . .

'She was so beautiful in her red checked skirt, Erol remembered. If only I'd kissed her that day. Now I'm going to go and die for no reason. How am I any different from a dog in the street? Before I've even kissed a girl, I'm going to die for nothing.

Fifth Tale: You've Been Called Up

Where am I going to die? On a mountain or in some quiet street that I've never seen before . . . No one will know I'm dead. As if anyone knows I'm alive! Why should anyone give a damn about my great plans! What will death be like? Will it be a void in the dark, dark underground?

Nothingness, I'm going to turn into nothing. But no one's aware of my existence now. But still . . . how can I die?'

Knock! Knock! Knock!

They knocked on your door. You were called up! You became a soldier. You died before you got to kiss any girls with long black hair.

Recite the Fatiha

You never did find out why you went to war or why you died. Your mother cried. No one else knew you existed. You are a national war hero. You've gone to heaven. All that remains to show you were once here is a tiny little street named after you.

War Hero Zafer Street

But, actually, that's not what happened. Zafer didn't die. At this moment he's fighting on the Besparmak mountain pass. At this very moment . . .

The asphalted road shook with the wheezy breathing of middle-aged men recovering from heart attacks. He understood immediately. The military vehicles were coming. He tried to keep a lookout from behind the rocks where he was hiding. He wished he could hide behind a thicket nearer the roadside. But there weren't any trees or thickets left since the bombings. The forest was like a ghostly vision with its bare, blackened arms outstretched. In that short moment when the planes had passed overhead, in that final instant when human beings and birds had shared the same fate there had been blood-curdling screams. Then the whole forest was silent. Then the sound of burning. And rain. And silence. In an attempt to hide from death, the chameleons had put on the black robes of death, but once they were on they had never been able to get them off again. After the fire ash poured down for days and the ensuing rain buried the charred seeds deep into the earth. If these seedlings ever grew again they would all sprout jet black.

A small army jeep was coming round the bend. The man jumped. Where are the heart-attack sufferers? He asked himself. They're wheezing and panting behind.

He took his Bren and straightened up. No, he shouldn't come out. Yes. He wouldn't come out. Could he come out? No. He came out.

The men in the jeep were struck dumb when they saw the man with the wild hair and beard who had emerged from the burnt forest and was using his Bren to signal them to stop. Good job the convoy was behind them! The man was smiling. He was wearing a brightly coloured shirt with flowers on it. His buttons were undone to the waist. 'What does he want?' they wondered. They couldn't tell. He was waving his hand and his Bren at the same time. It was just an instant. The men in the jeep couldn't speak to each other. They exchanged looks that said: 'Should we stop or shouldn't we?' The jeep stopped.

He immediately pointed his Bren at the men in the jeep, ready to shoot. He was saying something in Greek, talking very loudly and quickly. All they could understand was 'Turkokyprios.'

They replied in English. 'Yes, we are Turkish Cypriot.'

Now the man who had come out of the burnt forest started to speak English with a strong Greek Cypriot accent. They exchanged a mixture of half-Greek, half-English words.

'What's this Greek going on about? Is he asking about his children? Does he want to know what happened to his house and his village? Maybe . . . No, that's impossible! He's talking to us because he misses the sound of human voices. Even though he knows full well that he could die . . . He could kill us. The convoy's coming behind us. What if he surrendered? . . . He'll still die. He'd better not be trying to hide anything. Seeing as the first thing he asked us was whether we were Turkish Cypriot . . . Can we hide him? Is that what he wants? What then?' the men in the jeep asked themselves.

The man from the forest asked for a cigarette.

Fifth Tale: You've Been Called Up

A cigarette packet and lighter were held out to him; he hastily shoved them into his pocket. Clutching the Bren more tightly, he took a quick glance behind him.

'Are Youruks coming?'

The men in the jeep nodded in reply. 'The convoy of Turkish soldiers is coming, yes,' they said.

In that split second their eyes met. The man hesitated. He opened his eyes in amazement. Actually, no, his expression meant something different. He knit his brows as though he were crying. But, no, not even as though he were crying; his face showed the horror of a pain felt for the first time. A child's eyes looked back at the man. They gazed at each other for a moment that would stay engraved on their memories for ever.

'Oh my God!' shouted the man and started to head towards the rocks, his Bren still pointed at the men in the jeep. Nobody could understand why the man had looked at the young boy and shouted like that.

The convoy appeared. A Turkish officer jumped out of the vehicle at the front. He ran to the jeep.

'Was that a Greek Cypriot?'

'Yes, officer.'

'Was he armed?'

'Yes, officer.'

'Did he flee behind those rocks?'

'Yes, officer.'

They set up the bazookas and opened fire. Small rocks shattered like lumps of coal, scattering in all directions. The soldiers got out their trucks and took up position in the ditch beside the road. They fired without intermission. There was no sound from the man. He didn't shoot back or shout. The rocks became jagged where they had shattered, transformed into bizarre shapes. People passing that spot years later would never know how those rocks had come to have such weird shapes . . .

Zafer would never know whether or not the Greek Cypriot hiding behind the rocks had died. Why had he shouted 'Oh my God!' when he looked into Zafer's eyes? He'd never know.

Lefkosa–Ankara–Istanbul, 1975-1983

Draco Maturana Romesin
Second Baptism

Translated by Penny Rendall

Introduction by Penny Rendall

How should fiction deal with the horrors of murderous
dictatorships: the disappearances, torture and death; corrosive
fear, compromise and complicity; unimaginable courage;
survivor's guilt? So much 'material' for a writer, you'd think, such
powerful emotions, stories that reach into the very core of what
it is to be human. So where are the novels that tell it as it was in
Chile, Argentina and Uruguay in the 1970s and 1980s and of so
many other countries since?

The bald facts of those terrible years have been told in brave
testimonies to commissions and enquiries in the hope, still
unfulfilled, that once the truth was known, the guilty could be
brought to justice. These nightmare catalogues are there for
anyone with the stomach to read them.

But many of those who suffered cannot bring themselves to
speak of their experiences. And if you, as a writer, didn't suffer
personally, it can seem presumptuous to speak for those who did.
Add to this the sheer relief that it's over, the longing for a normal,
comfortable life after years of exile or fear of arrest, the calls not
to upset the fragile raft of compromises that is any return to
democracy. Those who care know what happened. Those who
pretended it wasn't happening, or thought it a just fight against a
few subversives and communists who deserved everything they
got, will remain deaf. It's not surprising, then, that much of the
writing that has been published is oblique or allegorical.

Draco Maturana's powerful, direct vignettes about people like

69

us, ordinary people in terrible circumstances, need no decoding. He has struggled to find a way to 'make the horror "legible"', as he puts it. At first he could only spew out undigested accounts of the brutal destruction of human beings. Only recently has he been able to write much more accessible stories, with glimpses of the love, hopes and dreams of the people subjected to the horror. A psychologist, he knows too well the effects on the human psyche. And is determined to make us understand too.

Here in Europe even those of us who demonstrated against Pinochet in 1973 or 1999 or were moved by the Mothers of the Plaza de Mayo were spared the saturation coverage as the gruesome testimonies emerged. We remain personally untouched by atrocities committed by regimes all over the world, often with the support of our freely elected governments. In the year when Amnesty reaches forty, when, in Chile, they have started locating, digging up and identifying the bodies buried more than a quarter of a century ago and when here in Britain our major political parties compete for the toughest policies against refugees, it seems we need more than ever straightforward human stories that help us begin to understand.

Translated text

He never let his feelings interfere with his actions. He'd always seen his body as a mechanism that allowed him to do some things and, occasionally, demanded from him or drove him to others.

Now, the sudden awareness of a cold wind on his face, the surprise of a starry sky when he opened his eyes after an age of blindfolds and hoods were wondrous sensations. He felt lost. Who was he? Where was he? The force of the wind on his face, a distant, persistent rumble and the jerk that slammed him into other bodies placed him at once. He was in an open truck. What was he doing there? Gradually his body started to impose its tyrannies: he was aching all over, his feet enormous, skin taut across his face. But – he wasn't there. There were no voices, no lights, he could open his eyes. He could only remember falling, like going to sleep when he was a little boy, falling into an endless black hole, where nothing mattered any more. Even as his body was disappearing he'd heard someone saying, 'You've gone too far again, fucking idiot . . .'

And then nothing.

He wasn't there now.

He was on the road in an open truck. Open? Sure. Why not?

It must be after curfew. He looked at the moonless sky. Orion was very high; there were the three stars of his belt . . . his knowledge of astronomy told him it was very late. Who was he with? Who were these other silent bodies next to him? Bodies?

The answer rushed in with a shudder: they were corpses, other corpses.

His wasn't the only death in those days. It was all perfectly clear, the corpses had to be buried, and he with them. The wind on his face, the stars, his body demanded he live. He didn't like the idea of being buried, either alone or with others. How could he escape? It'd be insane to jump off a lorry at fifty miles an hour or more. What else could he do?

He turned his head – cautiously, someone might be watching. He saw two soldiers, standing behind the cabin, their backs to him, sub-machine guns under their arms.

Escape didn't seem possible. Could he even move? Could he trust his body?

With pleasure, with surprise, he checked it out. First one arm, a hand, then the other; one leg, the other. He clenched his toes, breathed deeply. It all worked. He'd never imagined taking pleasure in pain, pain which told him now that everything was in its proper place, hurting but working.

Suddenly he heard thumps on the cabin roof. One of the soldiers yelled, 'Stop. Stop.'

'What's up?' another voice asked.

'I need a shit. I can't hold on any longer,' the soldier shouted.

The truck halted. The soldier, all tangled up with his sub-machine gun, got down and went to the side of the road.

'Cut the lights,' he shouted.

'Look at the bastard. Thinks we 'aven't got prettier arses to look at,' the voice said as the lights went off.

This was his chance. Slowly, he crawled over the other bodies. The headlights came on, illuminating the squatting soldier.

'Stop fucking about.'

In reply, a guffaw and a crude joke. The lights snapped off.

He made it to the side of the lorry. Did he have the strength to let himself down without making a noise? No choice. He tried. The lights came on again, showing the soldier wiping himself with a handful of leaves. More jokes and raucous laughter. The lights went off.

He managed to get himself down next to the back wheel and started to roll towards the verge, while another flash and more laughter swamped the night.

The soldier climbed back on to the truck. A single roll to go. The engine started. One more turn and he fell, with a loud splash, into a ditch by the side of the road. He shivered from both shock and terror; the noise carried clearly to the two soldiers behind the cabin.

'What was that? One of the stiff's fallen off?' one said.

The truck was already moving. They all just wanted to get the job done.

'Is it there? Who cares anyway? No one's going to count them.'

The cold water flowing over my body, soaking my clothes, stroking me all over reawakened my consciousness of life. I lay there quietly as the truck disappeared into the distance, as the engine noise changed to the whine of crickets and the glare of the headlights gave way to the sparkle of stars. I felt newborn and just baptised.

I stood up. I had my whole life ahead of me.

(Besides, no one knew who I was.)

Neil Grimmett
Wheelbarrow

W e'd christened him 'Wheelbarrow' because when he walked it appeared as if he was shoving an invisible one along. It was as if in reaction to his great intellect and physical frailty some dumb ancestor wanted him to recall the shape of toil. He was a scientist and spoke way above our heads. Even in normal conversations he liked to spend all those ten-dollar words. Then one day our chargehand, an ex-cook from Hong Kong, had enough. 'I know a fucking big word too,' he said, 'in-cor-por-a-tor.'

That was the piece of machinery we were running at the time. Wheelbarrow just looked at him and headed off, pushing his imaginary load then dropping in to see the principal foreman in charge of production workers. Within a week the overweight and near-retirement-age 'Hong Kong' had been transferred to being chargehand in charge of loading the train. A job known to break the backs and hearts of the fittest. And I had become the youngest chargehand in the factory's history and with too many lessons still unlearned.

Wheelbarrow got round to initiating me in his own way: by spraying one of my crew with dilute nitric acid and letting me get carpeted for it. Now, there's a funny thing about some acids: the weaker, more diluted they are, the quicker and meaner they can burn you. The viscosity of concentrated acid helps give you a little time to get the stuff off. Mind you, if you take too long and it does get in, it likes to find bone and keep gnawing.

Along with my promotion I had been moved into the big new nitration house. The hot seat you might say, and in more ways

73

than one. After our trial run, when things had gone wrong – luckily in a small, unspectacular way – we ended up with the stainless steel vessels in which the nitrous body comes alive and is caressed toward completion covered in a layer of drying explosive crystals. Not a nice thing to try and dislodge. Hard plastic and non-ferrous metal scrapers are about as risky as you dare. If I tell you that these vessels are big enough for you to drown in while stood up side by side with four or five of your mates and there are eight of them, then you might get an idea of how much scraping and daring was going to be required.

I was sitting in the control room, which is an air-conditioned glass bubble right smack in the middle of all the action. One floor up with all the pipes and their fluids pumping away under your feet and surrounded by forty-odd tons of acid bubbling and fuming its way along to becoming flakes of TNT. The desk in front of me is bigger and with more controls than any fancy recording studio you've ever seen, and behind my head there are banks of alarm panels full of hundreds of small black squares that can go red and scream their warning into you. The air in the cabin is pumped in from outside the huge mound that surrounds this building: it comes through filters and tastes sterile and nothing like the world outside.

I could see my crew outside, scraping away. On the floor of the cabin are the escape masks and small air bottles ready for if it becomes necessary to evacuate after we've dropped the charge into the massive drowning tanks below each vessel. I have seven men in my crew plus a chemist and often some bod from the Ministry of Defence. There are three masks – it could be fun.

Not that it much mattered. If we do drown this lot it apparently – they did it once on an island off Australia – goes off something like a red atomic bomb, then floats back down as a shroud and stays awhile. So you can sit in this cabin waiting for the filters to clog and start letting nitrous fumes et cetera fill the place up, or you can grab a mask with its couple of minutes air supply and try running down the steep flights of steel stairs and then find your way out through a labyrinth of pipes and tunnels to a place which looks, smells and tastes like an upturned witch's cauldron.

Luckily for me, I don't have to make the choice: chargehand

and chemist stay. To leave an explosive building before it is completely secure is a court-martial offence – and not very British to boot. Me and Wheelbarrow going down with the ship and me needing a fucking dictionary to understand his dying words.

I watched him walking round and round the cabin. Then he came in.

'Michael,' he said, 'I've been thinking.'

And that was always bad news.

He didn't care for the time that it was taking to get cleaned up. He wanted to get the next run underway so that *he* could get things put right. Wheelbarrow had worked out scientifically that weak nitric acid will dissolve the crystal and flush it gently out into the tanks. He will have a pipe connected to one of the feed lines of dilute nitric acid and then spray it over the contamination.

He looked at me as if I should be joining in with his boyish excitement at the idea. It is my job to make the final decision about everything that's not written in the operating instructions. Wheelbarrow outranks me by a million miles, is paid ten times what I earn and has no doubt forgotten more than I will ever know about the science behind this madness. But I get to carry the can.

All he wanted was a member of the crew to stand outside the cabin as he was doing the job to make certain that nobody came walking in or that he didn't get tangled up. Just an observer was all.

I brought the rest of my crew into the cabin and told them what was going to happen. We all watched as Wheelbarrow got an engineer to come in and make the connection to the feed line. Then I had to pick someone to go out while the rest of us sat nice and comfy and took in the show.

I sent my leading hand, Kirk. I did it because my wife had told me that his wife was shagging their fifteen-year-old paperboy. She was doing it every single chance she got, secure in the knowledge that once Kirk was inside this security zone he wasn't going to get out until the end of the shift. You don't want rescue services searching the ruins for someone who had slipped out unknown. Kirk and his wife have four kids and I had already decided, in this new position of power, not to allow any feelings of sympathy to influence my decisions.

Wheelbarrow dressed like a spaceman, appeared, and picked up the black rubber pipe. He gave the thumbs-up to Kirk who hit the pump button. The hose instantly turned into a snake: a spitting cobra. It was the pressure the acid was delivered at that did it, combined with the feeble little hands trying to control its whipping movement. I watched them in slow motion as Wheelbarrow struggled to gain control and Kirk tried to find the stop button. I say tried because most of the acid was hitting him in the face.

In this new multimillion-pound complex we had a load of old enamelled bathtubs filled with freezing and stained water. If you get splashed with acid you're supposed to submerge the limb in the water and rinse it nice and clean. Three of us ended up grabbing Kirk and plunging him bodily into one of the tubs. He'd tried to run for it in panic but pulled his goggles off first and the acid covering his hat and hair had blinded him. So we caught him. He fought like fury, thrashing and even trying to swim as we kept dunking him under. When one of the crew took my place on his arm I grabbed two of the special eyewash solution bottles and went to work on his eyes. I had to take my protective gauntlets off to do it and within seconds my forearms and hands were being eaten by what felt like a swarm of hungry, angry ants. But I couldn't bear to stop squeezing that liquid into his eyes, not even for the time it would take to give my arms a nice cold splash.

The whole time that this was going on, Wheelbarrow just stood there watching, his little white-booted feet protected and in a pool of acid.

Afterwards, he never said a thing. No word of apology or regret. As an experiment that might have worked was, I guess, how he viewed it. The union did try and do something about it but Kirk should have been wearing a full protective suit; his chargehand should have made sure that he was.

'You were lucky not to lose your stripes,' was the whisper the foreman gave me after the inquiry.

I went round to visit Kirk with two of the crew. His fat but pretty wife managed to crush one of her tits against my hand as she reached to wipe the stream of tears that wouldn't stop flowing from his permanently damaged eyes. She told us that he had said he was glad he wouldn't be coming back and did we know that he'd be home and would need her to look after him all the time. I thought I saw him smile at that but it may just have been the shape of his new features.

We get the first full production run underway and I get a new leading hand and a trainee.

The leading hand, Rikki, is an ex-marine and tough. I get on great with him and know that he took it all about as seriously as was necessary. He lived in a house on a cliff with a blonde opera singer and told us that they liked to lie in bed all day exploring each other's bodies and drinking bottles of iced Sancerre. Wheelbarrow was in the cabin with us and listened to this bit of information as if it was a lecture on primates. Rikki watched him walk out of the cabin and start trundling around in his red gauntlets and goggles, taking samples from the nitrators. He left just as Rikki got on to the *Blonde Bomb's* breathing technique when it came to oral sex. 'That is one dangerous son of a bitch,' Rikki gasped.

The trainee, Carl Maldoon, was about five foot four and weighed in at seven stone soaking wet; and he was scared. It pays to be a little nervous – complacency and all that. But scared is worse – it is a disease that can spread too easily into panic. I tried to find out why the hell he had come to this place and the closest I could get was that his wife thought it would be a good idea. Then one of the boys said they had seen him out with his wife and mother-in-law. The wife was a big, brutal-looking German, her mother made her look like a sweetie. They had Carl carrying this fat basset because it had become too tired to keep going. According to the tale, Carl was red-faced and staggering and only too glad to stop and talk. Which was unusual because he hardly ever spoke and when he did it was in a whisper that made you ask him to repeat everything about three times. It drove you wild on an irritable, long night-shift.

Rikki had had enough. 'Speak up, you cowardly little shitbird,' he yelled. 'Do you think the sound of your voice is going to set this stuff off?'

Rikki had already christened Carl 'Whispering Maldoon'. He

didn't like him – a sentiment voiced by the rest of the crew and understandable when you needed to convince yourself that all of your mates could and would pull you out of the deepest trouble.

I sent Maldoon out to do some samples and let Rikki cool down before things got ugly. Any fighting on the plant means instant dismissal for all parties concerned and I had seen Wheelbarrow taking note. He looked at Rikki in that superior *you got it wrong and I'm going to set you straight* way he had.

'It might be,' Wheelbarrow said, 'that Carl has hypersensitive hearing. It may even be that he believes we are all shouting at him every time one of us speaks.'

Well, I reckon the picture of Maldoon believing we were all mad at him about something he did not know and were all yelling at him all of the time must have struck everyone in that cabin at about the same moment – the laughter was nonstop.

Wheelbarrow stood there observing us as if we were crazy. When the noise died down a little he tried again. 'I can assure you all that the condition of hypersensitive hearing does exist and that it would probably be possible to treat it.'

We all started up again and Wheelbarrow walked out. I had a message waiting in the foreman's office at the end of the shift stating: 'If *anyone* is disrespectful to the senior chemist on duty, then they will be placed on a charge.' And that just about summed up our relationship with Wheelbarrow.

There was something, though. He always got the production up to maximum and was never too tired to sort something out or give you a full explanation about anything. It was all magnets and no miracles when he finished. And you knew that when it came to a crisis he was going to be as cool as liquid nitrogen.

The boys had taken to scaring Maldoon, dropping things on the steel decking behind him or dripping water on him if he was below them and yelling, 'Acid.' Or their favourite: setting off the 'test' on the alarm panels. There were three banks of alarm panels and on each of them about one hundred individual small squares. When a temperature started to climb, or a feed got a little low, or a seagull somewhere over the Bristol Channel cried 'quark' too loudly, then one of them lit up. Sometimes you might end up with three or four of them going at the same time with their accompanying audible warnings filling the cabin and everyone rushing around twiddling knobs and sliders, trying to calm the dragon.

Also, there was a small test button for the engineers to see that all the alarm panels had bulbs and songs in their hearts. It was an infamous way of waking up a dozing member of your crew or testing the bottle of a newcomer. To suddenly see every alarm in the place pulsing blood red and wailing like a hundred banshees was a real shock the first couple of times it caught you out. Maldoon went for it every time, though, and badly.

Then there were Wheelbarrow's lectures. One of the crew would get him started when Maldoon was stuck in the cabin with me teaching him panel control. Some stupid leading question about the effect of nitric-fume poisoning; or the accumulation of TNT in the blood system. And of course Wheelbarrow would give you every little detail until you could feel yourself dying.

Maldoon brought the worst on himself. Was it true, he asked Wheelbarrow, about a toluene fire? And Wheelbarrow told him that yes, it was true. A toluene fire did indeed burn with an invisible flame and you could open a door and walk into its embrace without seeing it was alive. Given the amount of that stuff we were always spilling, I could see that everyone was shocked.

But Maldoon was petrified. I followed him back along the tunnels a couple of times after meal breaks or at the start of a new shift and watched him fiddling about with his boots or safety clothing outside the doors, waiting for Rikki or me to stroll in front of him like a fucking mine-sweeper or something. I knew he wasn't going to last a lot longer but still felt reluctant to be the one to finish it. The foreman had a talk with me. 'Did you want me to get rid of Carl?' he asked. One bad word from the chargehand about any member of his crew was all it ever took. Rikki and the rest of the boys got to hear about it and started going around slapping each other on the back. 'I'm giving him more time,' I told them. I could see them trying to pluck up the courage to argue. I let the foreman know my decision and he gave me a sly wink. Our foreman once went through the fire and he was a wise old man.

Wheelbarrow

I was alone in the cabin with Wheelbarrow and Maldoon – everyone else had gone off to first break. I sent Maldoon down to ground level to take a couple of samples and then I stepped outside the cabin to do a couple of quick checks. And everything went to hell.

The steel floor under my feet began to tremble, then shake. A low-pitched growl became a deafening roar. I stared back into the cabin – which, in truth, I shouldn't have left – and saw Wheelbarrow's face. I'd never seen such a look of horror on anyone in my life. His face had gone white and his eyes were starting to bulge. My legs didn't want to support me and I had to struggle to get back into the cabin. The noise was getting louder and the building was moving as if an earthquake had hit.

'What the hell is it?' I said as I got through the cabin door. Wheelbarrow stayed frozen. Not one alarm light was lit – according to what was supposed to be one of the most sophisticated systems in the world everything was A-OK.

Then Wheelbarrow came alive. He rushed to the door and I knew straight away he was onto it. I watched as he left the cabin and reached the top of the stairway. Unbelievably, Maldoon was running up the stairs on his way to help. I had judged that he was about a mile away by now and going strong. Wheelbarrow tried to jump over him. The stairs sort of duck under the steel floor that the cabin is on, so if you were feeling frisky enough you could do a couple of chin-ups on the way down. Wheelbarrow inadvertently headbutted the sharp edge and fell backwards, blood jetting out of his head as he hit the stairs. He staggered back to his feet and shouldered Maldoon aside as he dived down the rest of the flight. Even above the noise you could hear him smash his way out of the door and keep running.

'What's happening?' Maldoon asked, his voice almost clear enough to hear the words properly.

Whatever it was, it was getting worse, reaching the kind of intensity that you knew was going to end in the biggest way possible.

I smashed the glass case containing the emergency lever, ready to drown everything in one go. My hand closed around the smooth red handle and the gleaming steel rod. I glimpsed that red mushroom about to fill our lives and I hesitated.

'It's the stirrers,' Maldoon said. 'They're not moving.'

I looked out and he was right. The enormous driving-shaft that runs the length of the building was still turning but each stirrer, dropping via its gears and bearings into the vessel, was still. I pressed the stirrer stop button. And the most beautiful silence and stillness touched the two of us.

An oil flow had become blocked and the bearings had seized up. The engineers found it out during the inspection and said, as always after one of these near misses, that it was a miracle. This time that none of the hot steel had gone into the explosive and set the whole lot off.

All we got told was that Wheelbarrow had had a nervous breakdown and had been given a desk job. The foreman said me and Maldoon had done our duty and no more. A couple of months later a memo came from the official inquiry. It stated that if the chargehand *had* pulled the lever, then that would have been the correct action according to the rulebook. And that, in a place like this, would have been all that really mattered.

Lawrence Norfolk
'Speech of the Weather': Writers in Transit

Homer wandered. Shelley escaped. Byron, it is rumoured, wrote parts of *Don Juan* on horseback. Dickens toured, and the experience killed him. Considering that writing is essentially a stationary act, the historical mobility of writers should excite more surprise. The troubadours of thirteenth-century Provence famously did more walking than singing which is why as Ezra Pound tells us, 'so many canzos begin with speech of the weather'. This gadding about has undoubtedly contributed to the subtle smudges and smears which have coloured the image of the writer. The writer as vagrant or vagabond; the transient tramp, *le clochard avant la lettre*. Writers won't stay stay put.

To the Frankfurt Book Fair . . . It is eleven o'clock on 2 October 1992 and a young man is trying to explain in laborious and horribly mispronounced French why 13 July 1789 was the last date on which a well-educated man could believe it possible to know every fact in the world. He is being interviewed by an Austrian woman from a radio station and the young man is speaking French because ten minutes before he was trying to explain the same point to his prospective Parisian publisher and has forgotten to switch languages. He has forgotten to switch languages because twelve hours earlier he was in Washington, DC, and he has not slept for a little over thirty hours. He is either twenty-eight or twenty-nine years old; he's unsure about this because his birthday passed at some point during the flight and he swallowed two barbiturates on the plane. This is his fifth interview today, there are seven more to come, and a further dozen on the following day, after which he will get back on the

83

plane, fly to New York, then Denver, then Wisconsin, then Chicago and then London, the place he left five days ago, which happens to be where he lives. By then he will have travelled a little under 46,000 kilometres in a little over two weeks. He is white-faced, red-eyed and slightly deranged by jet lag. He is also, of course, me.

One of the defining features of modernity is movement; movement across borders, between languages, between cultures. Voltaire's strange, opportunistic peregrinations and Joyce's insouciant knocking about Europe (with an ever-growing family in tow) have at their root the same odd notion: that one can as easily be a writer in Trieste as Saint Petersburg or Paderborn or Copenhagen. Or, to take the idea further, that one can be a *better* writer in the place that you are going to than in the place you have left. Would Thomas Mann have been so good a writer if he had stayed in Germany? Context matters – a fact that all writers live with and hate – and this fact makes the refusal of some writers to move at all an important refusal. One thinks of Thomas Bernhard railing against his own self-imposed immobility.

Now, in the glow of the postmodern sunset, writers are taking flight again. They rise on wings of aluminium and hurtle about the skies at speeds of a thousand kilometres per hour. Taxis take them between hotels and railway stations. Translators take them between languages. They pack and unpack. They are on tour, out of the country, on the move. In German their prepositions invariably take the accusative. They travel further and faster than writers have ever travelled before: a vast flock whirling in loose formation around an ever-shrinking globe, scattering readings and interviews like droppings. At first glance it appears that nothing has really changed. Only the pace has quickened.

The image of the writer as a wandering scholar was once carried as a banner. Now it is worn as a glamorous disguise to conceal the disruption of a fundamental relationship. In the past it has always mattered where the writer was – otherwise, why travel at all? I am not sure that this is still true.

'So many canzos begin with speech of the weather . . .'

Rightly so, for the weather is always different and infinitely complex. But now? Speech of the weather has been replaced by speech of the tight schedule, of the cancelled flight, of the dysfunctional baggage carousel. Writers swap anecdotes between themselves entitled 'The Hotel From Hell' or 'The Worst Flight I Ever Took' but no one needs to listen to them. They are always the same and nearly every writer has experienced the same things. Nothing of any real interest has ever happened in an airport, and airports are notoriously all the same. To travel between identical hotels is to travel nowhere at all. The physical and intellectual effort and purpose implied by a journey have been noiselessly stripped away. Now there is only movement.

Before considering the more or less dismal implications of that point, I would like to describe the first motorhome: what North Americans now call a 'Recreational Vehicle', but which was initially dubbed a 'Roulotte'. It was nine metres long, two and a half wide, bodywork built by Lacoste, and it comprised a sitting room, bedroom, study and bathroom all built on a Saurer chassis. Its top speed was forty k.p.h. on the flat and the kitchen was towed behind it. It was first manufactured in 1924 for the incomparably strange French novelist Raymond Roussel. The reviewer for the *Revue du Touring Club de France* noted, 'This year, at the start of summer, M. Roussel took to the road to follow his wandering fancy, in search of constantly changing sensations.'

Imagine Roussel's chauffeur-driven wagon chugging along the roads of Europe: a mad version of Proust's cork-lined study with wheels. Within sits Monsieur Roussel, noting down his 'constantly changing sensations' as the landscape rolls past the window. I don't know what sensation he felt when it rained, but I believe that moment changed irreversibly the relationship between the travelling writer and the travelled world because Roussel didn't get wet.

Frankfurt again. It is now 1996. The vile spire of the Commerzbank is rising and I am back in a neonlit cubicle, telling a succession of tape recorders how a rhinoceros was transported by ship from India to the coast of Italy in 1515 as a present for the Pope. It strikes me now that the rhinoceros, which somehow contrives to die twice in the novel, only does so when it reaches land – in other words, when it stops moving. The autobiographical implications of this are a little alarming. I wish I could put the next point in a less obscure fashion. The travels of writers have become increasingly gestural and unreal because it is not really possible to travel quickly. Not as a writer.

To eat breakfast in Venice and supper on Venice Beach is to experience nothing more profound than jet lag. A twenty-city tour is of literary value only to the writers of hotel guides. The view from 10,000 metres is always much the same, but the problem is not just one of perception. Historically, writers have always sought out likenesses, correspondences, ways in which things are similar. They did this principally because things were dissimilar and because to find correspondences between things was to make them intelligible. It was an act of aggressive comprehension, a refusal to take the world at its own disorientating word. Now, and quite suddenly, the reverse has become true. To say, 'The interior of one Hilton is much like that of another' is uninteresting and unnecessary, mostly because it is true. Writers spend too much time in these generic environments – in departure lounges, airplane seats, taxis – the mutant descendants of Roussel's 'Roulotte'. One could, if one wished, become gloomy and defeatist about the cultural implications of this.

In December of 1996 a German journalist called Tilman Jens and I took a train to the Baltic island of Usedom, a taxi from the station to the hotel, where a film crew picked us up and drove us along the coast of the island to a point on the cliffs overlooking the sea. The wind, blowing from the north, quickly chilled us all to the bone. Looking out over the Baltic Sea one can easily imagine that one has reached the end of the world, but writers since Homer have been thinking that. I began to shiver. Then the light failed and it began to rain.

The idea of what a writer does – and where he or she goes to do it – has been narrowing in the last few decades. Perhaps it is time to re-emerge onto more exposed terrain. The weather, and so 'speech of the weather', persist. After the sterile comfort of a thousand hotels perhaps it is time once again to get wet.

Günther Kaip
Novak

Extracts translated by Mike Mitchell

Introduction by Mike Mitchell

Günther Kaip subtitled his novel *Novak* 'a grotesque'. Published in 1996, it is a collection of surreal, nightmarish, freudian, comic episodes with little narrative continuity. The unity is provided by the figure of Novak, an eternally optimistic underdog, always polite, full of understanding and good-will, and always the outsider, the loser, the victim.

The extracts below consist of the first five sections of the book and the last, in all about one tenth of the whole.

Translated text

It gave Novak a great sense of satisfaction whenever he came across his name in the newspaper during his daily hour in the coffee house.

'Aha,' he would think, 'I'm not alone, there's two of us,' and his mood would undergo a dramatic improvement. Taking heart, he would order his next coffee and resolve to remain a Novak.

'I am Novak,' he said to the waiter, who bent down and regarded him with amazement. 'Don't hold it against me. And no recrimination, I won't have it,' he added, when he noticed the waiter grimace in disgust and throw up. That attracted the attention of all the customers, of course, and they immediately got up and fled from the coffee house.

The only one to remain seated was a young woman with

butterflies soaring up from her blond hair.

Novak nodded to her and stood up, pushing aside the waiter, who was writhing in guilt on the floor, racked by uncontrollable sobbing. Novak was a regular, after all. For years his newspaper rustling and thoughtful look had contributed to the stability of the coffee house, giving him the right to preferential treatment. But Novak had no intention of insisting on that now. He freed himself from the waiter's hands, which were clamped round his ankles.

'Outrageous,' hissed Novak, sensing the hot breath of a revolutionary attitude. It stiffened his neck muscles, straightened his posture, and with a spring in his step he walked over to the young woman's table. His heart turned a somersault as he looked into the green shimmer of her eyes.

'I love you, miss,' he said in the excited tones of a revolutionary: for love is revolution, Novak realized. 'I have always loved you.'

The young woman shook her head and looked down at her lap where a man's head was rolling to and fro.

'He stepped on a butterfly,' she whispered. 'Help me, if you really love me,' she said, pointing to a cushion beside her.

She grasped Novak's hands. In that moment he loved her even more, picked up the cushion and pressed it as firmly as he could down onto her lap.

'He hasn't even combed his hair,' Novak panted. He increased the pressure, feeling himself a man. 'This doesn't happen every day,' he muttered, ignoring the wheezes coming from the head.

Novak started to sweat, drops were running down his forehead and falling straight into the hands of the young woman, who had formed them into a cup.

This lasted for five minutes and Novak only released the cushion when silence reigned and the man's limbs had stopped twitching.

'Thank you,' said the young woman, standing up. She looked sadly at the lifeless body under the table. She was trembling all over and put her hand on the place on her chest where her heart was beating.

'Now she means me,' thought Novak and moved one step closer.

'We'll see each other tomorrow. Be on time,' said the young

woman as she passed between the rows of tables on her way to the door, which Novak, a gentleman of the old school, held open for her.

Proudly he walked back to his table and opened a newspaper. On the second page he came across a Novak who had escaped after a bank robbery.

'Aha! That's a good sign,' he cried, looking absentmindedly at the waiter, who had crawled on all fours to the kitchen and was lying there, motionless.

Novak leapt up, danced round the tables, through the coffee house and out into the street and then – two hours had passed – around his wife, who watched her husband with a shake of her head but a smile on her face.

'Magnificent,' she said and put on her coat to go out. She stood in the open doorway looking in astonishment at Novak, who was running across the ceiling, clapping his hands and giving her encouraging winks.

Nothing could stop him now. He tried his hand at somersaults, attempted elaborate pirouettes, keeping his balance securely, jumped from the wardrobe to the glass-fronted cabinet, slid across the walls and finished off with a spin.

'Magnificent,' she murmured, unsure whether, under the circumstances, she should go out. But the thought that she could bring him back a present commensurate with the event sent her tripping down the stairs.

Novak leant against the wall, panting. He thought of the young woman and realized he had not asked her name.

'That was a mistake, unforgivable,' he muttered and went to look in the mirror.

'But I know you,' Novak said to his mirror image, which had its eyes closed. 'You're refusing to look at me,' he shouted and prepared to attack.

Suddenly his mirror image wobbled and toppled into his arms without warning. It was heavy, infinitely heavy, and Novak simply dropped it on the floor, where it shattered.

With difficulty he made it to the living room. Once more the sweat was dripping from his forehead, but there was no young woman here to catch the drops. Novak lay down on the floor and cried.

Novak

In his mind's eye he saw the young woman and his colleagues at work. They were whispering and giving him pitiful looks.

'And everything started so well,' thought Novak. 'It's just not fair.'

He stretched out his hands towards the young woman, but all he grasped was empty air. When he opened his eyes, he gave a start. The room was crowded with people. They stepped aside, making a corridor along which his wife came towards Novak. She was laughing and waving a bunch of flowers in her left hand.

'For you, darling. Just for you,' said his wife, then she turned to the young woman, threw her arms round her and kissed her.

Novak tried to sit up while the couple separated and turned towards him. The young woman ran her fingers through his hair and whispered, 'You're tired . . . go to sleep . . . remember our rendezvous.'

'Of course. You're quite right,' he meant to reply, but his eyes fell shut and he sank into the young woman's soft voice.

The passageway was dark and damp. The floor consisted of bare earth. There was a musty smell. Novak felt his way forward by the light of his torch, cursing that he had promised his wife he'd tidy up their cellar. Cobwebs clung to his face. The ground sloped slightly downward. Pipes as thick as his arm ran along the walls, dripping. The bricks were covered in mould.

Novak reached the end of the passage and opened the door to their cellar. It took minutes for his eyes to adjust to the darkness. He went in.

He remembered the room as smaller, not so rocky and cavernous, not so neat and tidy. Along the rear wall a tarpaulin covered objects lying underneath it. Novak could hear his own breathing change to a high-pitched whistling.

'This is not normal,' he said out loud and ducked beneath the echo of his voice which was coming at him from all sides.

Cautiously he went over to the tarpaulin and tore it aside. Underneath Novak had expected spiders and other insect life, perhaps a dead rat.

But lying there, packed close together, were rigid bodies, the bodies of schoolmates, colleagues and acquaintances whom he had forgotten because they were not important to him.

They turned their eyes towards him, dead and empty eyes. They ground their teeth and stuck out their tongues. Novak panicked and ran into the cellar walls from which lumps of plaster fell off. With their eyes boring into his back, he desperately tried to find the way out.

'But they're dead. Dead and buried long ago,' he said, trying to raise his spirits as he tripped over objects on the floor.

When he looked at the bodies again he noticed a change in their gestures and expressions. They were grinning and beckoning him over. A few even stood up but collapsed as soon as they were upright, then crumbled into piles of dust.

Novak took a step towards them, a stick in his hands, ready to hit out, but dropped it at once, pulled trumpets and drums out of his head and put on a deafening concert. The floor swayed, the wine bottles in the rack clinked, the cellar door tugged at its hinges, the torch went on and off, fell out of his hand and smashed to pieces against one of the walls.

Then, when Novak was sure his voice could not be heard above the tumult, he started to scream and jumped into one of the piles of sand, thrusting the stick into it. He spread the dust into every corner of the cellar and covered himself in it. He rolled on the floor, kicking his legs in the air, stood up, knocked over some stacked-up planks, smashed bottles of wine and only stopped when the swirling dust had settled.

Novak spread out the tarpaulin and covered the whole of the cellar floor with it.

'The shroud,' he said. Then he picked up his torch, which was undamaged, immediately found the way out, locked the door and followed the beam of light, which was hurrying on ahead. The ground sloped slightly upward. There was a musty smell.

In the courtyard Novak brushed the dust off his shirt and trousers, threw the key into the bin and went to the stairs, where he met the caretaker, who gave him a friendly *Hello*. Novak did not notice her, but went on up the stairs in the hope that his apartment lay within reach.

The lamps over the bar were switched on when Novak ordered

his fifth whisky. He was the only customer in the place and kept nodding to the barman's stories, saying, *yes*, *hmm*, or *that so*.

Novak had had too much to drink and found it difficult to keep his balance. In addition, he was desperately trying to find a story that had once happened to him. To loosen up his memory, he rotated his head, stretched his back up straight until the vertebrae cracked and then he swung his arms round in the air.

He wanted something he could use to counter the barman, anecdotes from his life, but nothing occurred to Novak that would have been worth mentioning, while the barman talked and talked, piled story upon story, watching Novak's contortions with a smile. He was just lowering his voice and rolling his eyes when Novak broke off his exercises, leant over the bar and shouted:

'This lust for stories, at best it's two or three things that have happened to a person, if at all!'

The barman looked up in surprise and fell silent at the sight of Novak clenching his hands into fists.

'Those are just standard samples of experience, not stories. That's enough!' Novak's voice ending in a squawk. He downed his whisky in one gulp, banged the glass on the bar and slipped off his stool.

He intended to leave the place as quickly as possible, but when he heard steps and the crash of the toilet door shutting, he turned round and went back. The barman had disappeared. From the toilet came a dull thud and shrill laughter.

'Strange,' thought Novak, then hurried to the toilet door and opened it cautiously. In the middle of the blue-tiled urinal floor lay the barman holding his stomach with both hands and with his knees drawn up. Beside him sat a transparent figure with a piece of paper fixed to its chest. On it was written in large letters: *I am his story. Ahoy! Ahoy!*

The figure was regarding Novak attentively.

'He was lying,' it said in earnest tones, pointing to the barman. It was writing in a notebook with a pencil, filling page after page with neat writing, while beside it the barman kept on groaning. Ignoring him, the figure rose and looked down at the barman, who was trying to lift his head.

It pointed at him, smiled and went over to Novak. It seemed

surprised that he was still there, looking at the barman, who was lying still.

'Can't you see you're in the way? Go now,' it whispered. Its face, with a terrifyingly resolute expression, was coming closer, already it was stretching out its arms towards Novak, who fled, slamming the toilet door behind him, out into the street, not stopping until the door of the bar was nothing but a tiny black rectangle.

He leant against the wall of a house and looked back, afraid that the figure might follow him. After nothing happened for a few minutes he decided to go home. He staggered at every step.

In spite of everything, he envied the barman his story, a story that belonged to him alone, even if it had an obvious tendency to violence.

Novak kept stopping in his tracks and turning round, hoping to discover his own story. But there was nothing there.

It was depressing, and if Novak hadn't learnt to control himself, he would have sunk to the ground and surrendered to unrestrained weeping.

'You just have to make a start. But how?' he thought.

Perhaps his own story would have comforted him or told him jokes to cheer him up. That would have calmed Novak down.

As it was, he walked straight past his house and out of the town, obsessed with the idea of finding his own story.

Yet all he had to do was to feel his left shoulder. There sat a figure busily writing in its notebook.

Novak could never claim that he was treated with consideration on his way to work. People, and there were a lot of them, stepped over him when he fell down, trampled on his stomach or shoved him without warning off the pavement and into the path of buses, which almost cost him his life every time. On seeing him, women pushing prams crossed over to the other side and infants shook their fist at him. But the most unbearable, as far as he was concerned, were those who simply dissolved into thin air before his eyes.

And Novak was such a harmless person. His colleagues at the office ignored this trait, squeezing tears of resignation and desperation out of his face and collecting his saline discharges in their teacups.

Novak

At lunch break, Novak attempted to get a meal.

'But you can't take the place away from someone else, a strong young man like you,' he heard the waiters say when he asked to be allowed to have a meal. 'A little more restraint, if you please. You're not the only person in the world.'

They were right, of course, even if he did think it was going a bit far to throw him out of the restaurant on to the pavement every time.

'Nevertheless, one day I'll be lucky,' Novak thought as he crossed the street and hurried up the steps to the office.

There his boss was waiting, arms crossed. He was angry, Novak could tell that at first glance, very angry even: he was hovering an inch above the ground.

'Too late,' he roared and pushed Novak so violently against the door post that he lost consciousness and sank down on to the parquet floor.

After that excitement he deserved a rest, all his colleagues were agreed on that, patted him on the shoulder, set him down at his desk and brought him their files with concerned looks on their faces. They stroked his hair, whispered encouragement and assured him they held him in high regard.

That usually lasted for five minutes, five minutes of balm for Novak, who recovered consciousness during these blandishments, so that his colleagues could go back to their card game with their minds at rest.

Novak frequently interrupted his work on the account books to feel his head, which had not suffered any damage. He made an effort to cheer his colleagues up with jokes, but they didn't notice, since the card game demanded their full attention.

After work Novak went out into the street whistling. He had got through a working day without serious damage, he still had arms and his head, which swayed in time with his steps.

Naturally that was a provocation, and a number of those hurrying past had to turn back to hit the smile, that early-evening irritation which was beyond forgiveness.

Novak accepted it, he understood his fellow men, whom he had brought into a dreadful situation with his inconsiderateness.

'After all, I'm part of society, I don't live alone,' he thought, guarding his face which was wet with blood, frightening some of those coming towards him. Others, for their part, kneaded his skullbones, pulled his cheeks tight or stretched them out and twisted his ears until they were satisfied with the result.

'Thanks,' Novak shouted after them, for he appreciated the fact that they had sacrificed valuable time for him.

And he would have gone on his way in carefree mood had it not been for the pain, the white-hot pain that brought tears to his eyes.

'Even that will change,' thought Novak and looked straight ahead, glad that that thought had occurred to him.

'Good morning,' said Novak to his wife before he sat down at the breakfast table. That was at six o'clock.

He bit firmly into a roll.

'Tastes good,' he said to his wife without raising his eyes. He chewed slowly, methodically.

His eating tackle was well serviced, the daily paper had reached eye level and rustled as he turned the page. That was at six thirty.

'The jam, please,' he said to his wife, starting with a shock of surprise when he noticed his wife wasn't there. That was at six forty-three.

One minute later he had so far recovered that he could immerse himself in the newspaper again. Now he was reading more quickly, not concentrating. That lasted from six forty-five until six forty-nine.

Suddenly he jumped up, ran round to the other side of the table and went to the balcony door. The sun was saying its morning litany, the heavens were intact. Crows were flying with tape measures to put figures on the distances.

'That's nice,' murmured Novak, impressed, stepping to one side as a high-speed train thundered past and disappeared into the bedroom. That was at six fifty-four.

Normally at this time Novak had finished his breakfast, the folded newspaper lay on top of his sandwiches in his briefcase, and his wife was standing by the door to kiss him goodbye. But something had gone wrong.

Novak scratched his head to facilitate thinking. However, as he touched one spot on the back, his whole head fell off his body straight into his lap. Novak looked down at it in astonishment, but immediately pulled himself together since it had often happened recently that his limbs broke off or he left a hand on his desk in the office.

But today was the first time for his head, and he needed that. There would be problems if he started going round headless.

'It was probably already loose,' thought Novak to calm himself down, and looked at the clock. It was five past seven. That irritated him.

'Such a little thing and I'll be late for the office,' he thought.

Resolutely he pressed his head on to his neck, jumped up on to his two feet and hurried to the front door. His wife was leaning against the door frame.

'Well, where on earth did she come from?' he muttered.

With a smile, he went up to his wife, spread out his arms and kissed her so clumsily on the lips that his head slipped on to his left shoulder.

'Comedian!' his wife called out after him as he hurried down the stairs, blushing as he straightened out his head.

Transparent webs formed between Novak's fingers. They tore, fluttering in the wind as his hands rose up and, fingers splayed, placed themselves on his face. Novak lost his balance. His right arm flailed around in the air, his trunk swayed to the left and right, while his legs tried to run away. There was no one at all to be seen, which was unusual on a Saturday morning.

'Something must have happened,' thought Novak.

The shops were shut, barricaded with planks of wood and crouching down behind rolls of barbed wire. The queasy feeling Novak had had in his stomach since wakening from a death-like sleep increased and slowly spread throughout his body.

Which was inconvenient, as he had prepared himself for a pleasant day devoted entirely to himself. After all, he had come to an understanding of many things, had both feet on the ground and had removed all obstacles, broadening the scope of his mental perspective. In a word, he embodied hope.

His body became weightless and hovered above the asphalt. He rose higher, as if he were being pulled up through the air on a rope.

'Is there more?' murmured Novak in astonishment. He was sure that in a few seconds he would wake up in bed, alone as his wife was away, with the sound of the alarm clock in his ear and the warm rays of the morning sun on his face.

At that moment his legs fell off his body on to the street, as did his arms, which flailed around in the air shortly before hitting the ground. It tickled, and Novak looked in astonishment at the stumps of his arms and legs, which weren't bleeding. The index and middle fingers of the right arm he had lost were spread out in a V: V for Victory.

His head was in its proper place and covered in sweat; his shirt was sticking to his skin and the coat he had bought yesterday was fluttering in the wind which was sweeping through the town.

'That's not fair,' he shouted when he finally realized it wasn't a dream and he had really been on his way to the supermarket to do his weekend shopping.

'What a time for this to happen to me,' he panted. His voice echoed down the ravines between the tall buildings; the roaring of the wind became so loud it hurt his ears.

Things that had been far away now seemed close to his ear: the jangle of the tram below him, the stuttering engine of a car, the sudden cry of a child in a park, the rustle of a macintosh, glass shattering, the town hall clock ticking a mile away, a telephone ringing, a computer humming as it was switched on, fat sizzling in a frying pan.

Every sound, every noise, was an explosion that startled Novak, who was flying up and down the street. Sometimes he dropped down in an air pocket, but before he hit the ground he was caught on an upcurrent which flung him back into the sky.

Suddenly it was silent and down on the footpath – he happened to be flying along the gutter of a house – he recognized his wife, Tamara, Kurt, Georg, the caretaker and her husband. They had linked arms and were crossing the street in close formation.

'You're staying, aren't you?' they called out to Novak.

Directly below him, outside a cake shop, Brustbein was just picking up one of his wife's white gloves.

'Come on,' she shouted up at Novak.

'And hurry up, if I may make so bold,' added Brustbein.

'Come on, never say die!' They were all trying to spur him on as they clapped their hands in time. 'Don't be afraid.'

'But it's too early,' thought Novak, who had allowed himself to be distracted and only just managed to avoid a pigeon crossing his flight path.

'Bravo!' came the cry from the street below. Novak felt flattered and performed a few somersaults in the air, though his lack of arms meant that the sleeves of his coat slapped him round the ears.

'Are we going for a meal?' he shouted when he had his flight under control once more. 'Or to the zoo? Perhaps to the fairground? You decide, I'll go along with whatever you want,' Novak shouted, but he realized they couldn't hear him – they'd gone into a restaurant while he was flying through the air and birds darkened the skies, while huge clouds of dust rose from the streets, bricks slowly floated up like balloons and disappeared in the black of the sky.

Novak pumped air into his lungs, pulled his head in and tried to become as small as one of the birds that accompanied him up there, hoping to lose all memory, all thought of his future, simply to be there, whatever might happen to him, and he felt feathers growing under his shirt, and in his chest was a bird's heart, transparent and warm, beating like mad.

But suddenly his flight came to an abrupt halt. He crashed into the air, simply got stuck, and when he panicked and looked down he saw the barman with his story on his shoulder. They were both watching Novak and whispering to each other while the barman held up a long pole on which an old man was balancing, arms outspread.

'You can't do anything without a pole,' the man called up sadly to Novak, who was still stuck above the street, level with the sixth storey. The old man jumped down on to the street, broke the pole the barman had dropped, and disappeared round the corner.

'Please stay,' Novak called after him, while the barman, his story sitting on his shoulder busily writing in a notepad, followed the old man.

Meanwhile, Novak's wife, Tamara, Kurt, Georg, Frau and Herr Brustbein, the caretaker and her husband had come out of the restaurant. In a good mood they looked up at the sky.

'Where is he? He can't even wait for us,' they said. 'How selfish can you get?'

'Here I am,' shouted Novak, but he was caught in a gust of wind. With his last reserves of strength he managed to hold on to a gutter. When he looked down he saw the young woman from the coffee house. Butterflies fluttered up to him from her hair.

'There, it worked out after all,' thought Novak. For a moment he forgot his precarious situation as the young woman saw him and shouted up to him, 'There you are at last!' and he shouted back, 'Of course,' and suddenly the gutter broke away from its fixing, a gust of wind flung him high into the air and carried him out of the town, towards the horizon. Novak was no longer pushing it away from him, now it was zooming towards him.

Juan Goytisolo
A Cock-Eyed Comedy

An extract translated by Peter Bush

Introduction by Peter Bush

Juan Goytisolo is Spain's leading contemporary writer, though he has not lived in Spain since 1956 when he went to Paris as a 'self-banished' Spaniard. Goytisolo was born in Barcelona in 1931 and experienced the rigours and cruelty of the civil war as the son of a minor industrialist. His mother was killed by an Italian Fascist bombing raid over the Catalan capital. He has recounted his life under Franco's dictatorship and his subsequent literary, sexual and political odyssey in two volumes of autobiography – *Forbidden Territory* and *Realms of Strife* (Quartet and North Point Press) – which were my first full-length translations. From the early 1960s, Goytisolo lived between Marrakesh and Paris and since the death of his wife, Monique Lange, he has spent most of his time in Morocco.

He maintains a dialogue with the Spanish reading public through regular contributions to the national daily, *El País*. These can be political journalism of striking originality as dispatches from the front (*Landscapes of War: From Sarajevo to Chechyna*, City Lights, 2000 and Middlesex University World Literature Series, 2001). There are also incisive polemical interventions, such as the recent 'It's downhill all the way', which attacked the dumbing down of Spanish intellectual and literary life and the responsibility therein of conglomerates such as the PRYSA group which owns *El País*. This essay – published in that newspaper – provoked a stream of attacks and counter-attacks in fierce debate in print, national radio and television: one palpable outcome was the appointment of a new literary editor for *El País* and the reconfiguring of its influential literary supplement. Then there is Goytisolo's role as chair of the UNESCO committee that seeks to defend the 'intangible' cultural traditions of humanity . . . Or his articles against racist attacks on gypsies and migrant workers in Spain and the racism of Fortress Europe.

Of course, the dialogue is mainly nourished through the literary texts which Juan Goytisolo has regularly published since his *Count Julian* trilogy (translated by Helen Lane). The present extract is from *Carajicomedia* (Seix Barral, 2000), published by Serpent's Tail in 2002 as *A Cock-Sure Comedy*. It ploughs a typically Goytisolian furrow: the fusion of a dialogue with literary works from the Spanish 'tree of literature', in this case, late medieval homoerotic texts written by priests, autobiographical elements, sexual and political politics all wrapped in a flow of carnivalesque, parodic prose springing from an idiosyncratic reading of *The Way*, the spiritual treatise of Monsignor Escrivá Balaguer, founder of the Opus Dei and currently en route to canonization. The narrator, le père de Trennes, is an Opus leader who lives various transmigrations of the soul that allow Goytisolo, among other things, a savage satire of the relationship between the Catholic church and homosexuality. As the Monsignor himself puts it in precept 193 in his section on mortification: 'Tender, soft, flabby . . . that's not the way I want you.'

Translated Text

The Poet and *le père de Trennes*

I

I had just written in my diary *the morning passed as usual, I was in the office*, an expression of disenchantment, after one of my tiresome nocturnal cruises through Panam's and the Cadiz when Pepe startled me with the news: there's a French gentleman on the line asking after you.

The little red light of danger flashed immediately. It couldn't be that dodgy translator of the Peninsula's hundred best resistance poets who delivered up his deadly verse on the tablets of print of *Les lettres françaises?*

'Who's that?'

'My real name is of no matter. Call me *le père de Trennes.*'

'Like Peyrefitte's character?'

'Just so. The one in *Les amitiés particulières.* An enchanting book, don't you agree? But I don't only read novels. I translate Cavafi in my moments of leisure. If you have a spare minute, I would be delighted to have coffee with you.'

I invited him home the following day, after checking that Gabriel and Cucú would be with me. They were as puzzled as I was. A polyglot priest and translator of Cavafi is not part of the daily offering, at least not in this needy Spain of ours. I postponed my visit to a nephew suffering from scarlet fever.

We were expecting, or rather I was, the visitation of a priest soutaned to his ankles, with all the attributes and trimmings of his office and corresponding sanctity. In his place, Pepe showed into the parlour a man in his forties, dressed executively, with a touch of that uneasy stiffness one finds in the upholders of evangelical missions who propagate their faith from door to door in Oxford. But it was a deceptive first impression soon belied by a coherent combination of detail: long, wavy hair, a halo of perfume or aftershave, a designer cravat, sveltely Italian shoes and silk socks. A discreet gold crucifix adorned his immaculate shirt front.

He introduced himself with a display of modesty: though a priest of the oriental rite the Pope had recommended to take the Virgin of Fatima to Russia, he was a member of the Opus Dei usually resident in Ai Monti Parioli. But he enjoyed, he hastened to add, a special dispensation. His linguistic expertise – in classical Greek and Aramaic – has converted him to a kind of itinerant ambassador for the Apostolic Prelature in the Near East.

'I have come to Rome at the invitation of a team of researchers from the Opus's university in Navarra. They have just scientifically proved the truth of the mystery of transubstantiation, the actual presence of Our Lord in a freshly consecrated wafer! A world first placing Spain in pole position among the most advanced societies, do you not think?'

Was he serious? Impossible to tell. His face was as wily as it was deadpan. He rambled on about friends held in common: Saint John of Barbès-Rochechouart, the young Philippine working for the state tobacco company who apparently was his servant. Then he tried to find out if I knew the Seminarist in the pink soutane.

'I don't know who you're talking about.'

'She insists you met her in a pious little café in the Barrio Chino. Can't you remember her? Well, she is a bit of a voyeur, maybe the encounter is a fantasy of hers.'

Silence ensued.

'Do you live in the Opus's residency?'

'Not at all! I sort myself out. I've rented a modest flat in San Gervasio. I'll move in on my return from the University of Navarra.'

(When I later visited him, he showed me into a sitting room of an unmistakably 1960s bourgeois vintage, with its green-upholstered three-piece suite, marble side table littered in medical advice journals, grey moquette and a four-branched chandelier. Everything exuded conventionality and inane riches: a well-stocked larder and wardrobe, austerely beautiful images and crucifixes and the devoted care of the blessed cleaning ladies or lifelong assistants, as the Father called them. On the table in his office, next to the Kempis of our era, the statuette of a Greek ephebe stood nevertheless erect.)

Gabriel, Cucú and I were highly intrigued, pricked by a somewhat perverse curiosity towards this character's ways and by-ways. Was he? Of course he was or, as I recalled quoting Lorca, he was wasting his time. His suave gestures and religious unction were criss-crossed by titters and the fleeting frisson of guilt of someone afraid of showing his hand and exercising reserve. Cavafi and the Hellenic adolescents seemed more a decoy than an admission. *Il avouait peut-être les télégraphistes pour ne pas parler des facteurs!*

I invited him to come on another afternoon for drinks with my publisher and his Icelandic friend. He alleged, as if scenting danger, an unavoidable appointment with someone close to the

Monseigneur, but he finally accepted.

'Chartreuse, Benedictine?'

'My aunts, may they rest in peace, would call that a tot. I'm not sure if it was a digestif or anis.'

'Take your pick from the bottles in the cabinet. Pepe, serve the gentleman.'

After a brief whisper, *père de Trennes* opted for a gin-tonic.

'Careful, don't overdo the gin or I'll get tipsy,' he warned.

Precisely what I wanted, to get him tipsy, as he put it, and go on a fling accompanied by his holiness in the bars on the Rambla and Escudillers. My publisher made sure his glass was full and with peasant cunning, we egged him on.

Were the rumours right about the Monseigneur's life and miracles: on his charismatic appearances in a black Cadillac and nouveau-riche fondness for giving audiences in rooms lined in silk with enamelled chests, glass cases of Chinese ivory carvings, bronze lamps and clocks, *coromandel* screens, coats of arms? Was it really true that a kneeling maiden placed a silver tray on the table with his correspondence while Monseigneur breakfasted with customary frugality?

'Uff!' responded *père de Trennes*. 'A load of envious gossip mongering! Fishwives at it! The Father's precepts of simplicity and humility give the lie to those malign allegations.'

But the gin-tonics were taking their toll and, when Cucú and Colita arrived, *père de Trennes* agreed to dance a paso doble with them. It was the one I'd listened to as a child in the fiestas in La Nava. I sometimes liked to listen to it in the background, as a counterpoint to my translation of Eliot or, in the company of some pretty boy, on the jukebox in Panam's. A fifth or sixth sense (inevitably the sixth!) hinted it would be a night to remember and it was. A sudden excitement had gripped everyone, as if we'd all taken on the deep truth in these lines by Verlaine:

> *N'as-tu pas fouillant en les recoins de ton âme*
> *Un beau vice à tirer comme un sabre au soleil?*

I turned up the volume *ex profeso* (my parents were out of town and Pepe had beat a tactful retreat). The rhythm of the paso doble gradually raised the emotional pitch: our respectable family sitting room seemed more like a ring at the fair or a bull-run. Colita brandished with brio Cucú's cravat and she'd purloined a pair of fans from the glass case, now whirled them like banderillas. Then, *père de Trennes* became the Miura. A red quilt! I fetched a faded pink one which I handed to Colita. The good priest pawed the carpet with his elegant hoofs before making for the cloth. Cucú goaded him roaring like a lioness in heat. Our noble young bull wasn't afraid of ridicule. Red in the face and a little unbuttoned, he followed the script with the passion of the possessed. The paso doble turned us on: nothing was more arousing than its crescendo well watered with gin. After a few minutes we felt exhausted. *Père de Trennes* wrapped the pink quilt round his shoulders and asked, 'How'd I be as a dancer?' 'A real hit,' said Colita. He tried a few steps, but he couldn't. The regularly poured gin-tonics had made their mark. He was drunk and started to sing.

(It was one of the ditties his 'colleagues' used to sing in the sense that term carries in the Moroccan dialect of Arabic.)

He didn't resist being bundled into our cortège of two taxis to the beaches of shifting sand at Panam's. There we served him two more rounds of his favourite drink and I introduced him to a well-dressed hunk with the manners of a private-school pupil. But my brokering failed. *Père de Trennes* showed not the slightest interest in the youth. Perhaps he liked adolescents like the poet he translated or moustachioed beefcake with the looks of a security guard. There were no specimens of either variety in that dive. The mystery persisted although, as Gabriel said subsequently, *ce qui est sûr c'est que s'il joint les mains pour prier, il entrouvre au même temps autre chose!*

What happened afterwards in the early hours I could only recall later in the depths of my hangover. I went to the Hotel Cosmos with the spurned youth (a good professional, but no real conviction), my publisher and his friend escorted *père de Trennes* to the flat in San Gervasio. They had to help him out of the taxi: he'd got hiccups and was sobbing hysterically: *That is quite finished! Never more! Mon Dieu, quelle déchéance!* The door had to be opened for him (apparently he couldn't hit the keyhole). Then they dissolved two Alka Seltzers in a glass of water and settled him in bed.

Writing these lines, I remembered a few lines by Cavafi, probably translated by the Father:

*And how dreadful the day when you give in
(the day you let yourself go, and you give in).*

2

For a number of years I lost sight of the good *père de Trennes*.

I found out he'd gone to Cuba to greet Fidel Castro's revolution. By all accounts he sang the praise of its portents and marvels. Perhaps he liked mulattos? Wagging tongues reckoned he did: 'As a real saint, he goes after the all-healing syrup of the Lucumi. *On l'appelle déjà l'Abbesse de Castro!*'

Back in Europe, he set up in Paris. I'd got him the address on the Rue Poissonnière and supposed he was in contact with Juan though neither mentioned the other to me. The almost painful, whole-hearted energy I seek in bed no longer spurred me on as before. Was I getting old? Yes, I probably was.

Fortunately, that biological process is accompanied by greater mental strength and also greater calm and confidence. Marguerite Yourcenar, whose work I plunged into after shelving de Beauvoir, expresses it very well in a quotation taken, like the one from Verlaine, from Robert Liddell's excellent biography of Cavafi which the priest lent me:

*L'angoisse, en matière sensuelle, est presque toujours un
                                        phenomène de
jeunesse; ou elle détruit un être, ou elle diminue
                                        progressivement du fait de
l'expérience, d'une plus juste connaissance du monde, et plus
                                        simplement de
l'habitude.*

But to return to *père de Trennes*. He occasionally phoned me at the office: *Ah, comme je vous sens heureux respirant l'air des ramblas! Ici, il pleut dans la ville, et il pleut dans mon coeur, comme dit Brassens.*

A Cock-Eyed Comedy

Envoyez-moi un petit rayon de soleil: un poème, une lettre, une photo de vous accompagnée d'un beau garçon! After his rash of Castroism, he prudently steered away from politics and revolutionary ideals. Nor did he tramp Via Vitrubio or, very exceptionally, the Via Bruno Buozzi. According to Juan, he lived a life of dedication to his apostolic endeavours in places of very dubious sanctity.

One day he turned up at my flat in Turó Park: unharmed by the passing of time, long-haired and dressed with an elegant insouciance, very *soixante-huitard*. (A few weeks before he'd called me excitedly from Cairo: he'd just opened his heart to a traffic cop in the busiest square in the city! What had been his response? 'Oh, he was perfect! He went on with his whistle but agreed to meet me in the front of the Egyptian Museum.' He sighed: so tall and strong, his feet like a grape-picker's out of Velásquez.)

'You look as fresh as a daisy! Are you on a course of hormones in the fatherland of Ceausescu?

'I don't need to go to Romania like some television announcer. I try to live a healthy life while waiting for my next reincarnation.'

He'd finally found his sense of humour. He told me about his new friends in Paris: Severo, Roland, François Wahl. What about Genet? *Il l'adorait de loin, mais ses manières brusques l'intimidaient.* As for his relationship with the Rue Poissonnière he suffered from Juan's up-and-down moods, 'ever more engrossed in himself and his labyrinthine writing'.

He was apparently preparing – or perpetrating a novel – that the author himself dubbed a door-stopper, tome or artefact – whose production required extensive reading and years of labour. A history of sexuality in the light of Catholic doctrine via a journey through the Spanish language from the Middle Ages to the present. He wanted to transcribe his cruising experiences in church language, including that of the author of the contemporary *Kempis*, in order to parody it from within and strip bare its hypocrisy: what, perhaps contaminated by dipping into TelQuel writings, he called 'textual libido'. We both laughed.

'Is it an autobiography or a novel? Is there a plot, chapters, real people?'

Plot is the least of his worries, the *père de Trennes* argued at second remove. Our mutual friend is trying to train his ear to catch the voices from the past in order to appropriate them and become lord and master of his writing, forgetting those striving to do that in relation to literature and literary life. Thus an artist's vitality would be measured by his ability to assimilate the different literary tendencies of the tradition in which he is inscribed at the behest of a vast, ambitious and original project (didn't Eliot write something similar?) Whoever bypassed this substratum or digested library, *jamais en rapport avec les combinaisons mercantiles* (to quote Mallarmé), was condemned to live and disappear with his era . . . *Père de Trennes* doubted the viability of the undertaking and so did I. Challenged to choose between Forster and Bakhtin, I always opt for Forster and his reasonable precepts and parameters. But I was awaiting an opportunity to discuss it with Juan.

'*Et vous, mon père?*' (I always address him as *vous* in order to mortify him.) 'How's life treating you round Barbès and the Gare du Nord?'

'I've ceased to be *le père de Trennes*!'

I'd served him gin on the rocks and he savoured it on his palate.

'*J'ai changé mon nom de guerre, comme les cocottes d'antan!* Now I'm Brother Bugeo. Doesn't it ring any bells?'

It did really, but it wouldn't come to mind.

'He wrote the *Cock-Sure Comedy*, a work of saintly shamelessness, a short, sharp exchange included in the *Book of Comic Songs*. Don't you recognize it?'

The anachronisms of ex-*père de Trennes* and greenhorn Brother Bugeo delighted me. Had he, as he advised Juan, finally taken up the English literary tradition from Sterne to Swift? I remember we bantered about his longevity. A century and a half? From the early Middle Ages! We lingered on Jehovah's fantastic computations and the earthly affections of the patriarchs in Genesis. He quoted lines of Milton at me and I replied with an aphorism from Gracián. It ended in stalemate.

He poured himself another gin with lots of ice.

'Let's not beat about the bush,' he said very seriously. 'Don't you believe in transmigration?'

ropelights – drw <info@thefreeflowstudio.co.uk>

Stefano Benni
The Discombobulous Worm
(The Tale of the Black Dog)
An extract from The Bar under the Sea
Translated by Carol O'Sullivan

Introduction by Carol O'Sullivan

Stefano Benni was born in Bologna in 1947. He is the author of six novels, several collections of short stories and vignettes, three volumes of poetry, a volume of collected plays and an illustrated comic bestiary, all published by the Milanese publishing house Giangiacomo Feltrinelli. He is also well known as a journalist and his writing has appeared in several prominent Italian periodicals including *Panorama*. Benni's work is characterised by political and social satire as well as by a dense web of intertextual reference. *The Bar Under The Sea* (*Il Bar sotto il mare*, 1987), from which this story is taken, is a collection of stories told one night by the patrons of the eponymous bar, among them a certain black dog.

Translated Text

En royal manteau blanc tout luisant, onde et flamme: C'est la Mite.

(In royal white mantle, wave and flame, shining: It is the Worm.)

– Paul Verlaine

Of all the animals which infest the pages of books, the discombobulous worm is certainly the most harmful. None of its colleagues even comes close. Not even the bedbug *Cimex*

The Discombobulous Worm

Capitalophagus, which eats capital letters, or the buterfly, a small member of the *Hymenopterae* which eats double letters, preferring the 'mm's and the 'nn's, and which adores words like 'committee', 'millennium' and 'accommodation'.

A fussier beast altogether is the punctuative or Dublin termite which nibbles away full stops and commas to cause the famous stream of consciousness torment and delight of typographers and literary critics the world over

The spider à parole unique, or *Arachnis Univerbus*, is now extraordinarily rare. It gets its amusing name from the fact that it eats only one word, 'serjaunty'. This tiny spider is only found in elderly texts on feudal land law as the word has otherwise fallen into disuse, and the few examples extant have been decimated by the spider.

I would like to mention two other common biblianimals: the subjunctive flea and the assibilant, or lisper fly. The former eats only subjunctives in all their persons but especially in the first person singular. Newspaper articles which seem somewhat ungrammatical might in fact have been attacked by the subjunctive flea, says the journalist what he wills. *Assibilans*, on the other hand, mostly eats the 's's from the ends of verbs and excretes them as 'th's. Thus doth, saith, (et thetera). In the seventeenth century there were millions of them, though now they are increasingly rare.

But as I was saying before, of all the biblianimals the discombobulous or trader worm is by far the most harmful. It usually attacks towards the end of the text It takes a word and puts it in the place of another, and puts the latter back in the place of the exchanging. The changes are minimal, sometimes the worm is satisfied with former three or worm words, but the results are logic. The text loses all devastatating and only after a evil investigation is it possible to reconstruct it as it was before the wish of the discombobulous worm

Way the worm should act in this why, if according to the instinct of its meticulous nature or because it hates literature, we do not can. We know only express one fervent intervention: may you never chance to fall upon a page marked by the passage of the discombobulous four.

Hannah Crow
Gerald at the Colonic Club

O ne time I was renting a room in the back of a Greek
restaurant. The noise got bad when the dancing started but
they were always giving me leftover scraps of lamb and so forth,
and about that time I didn't have much money. There was one
condition with the room. I had to go and collect the rents from
the owner's tenants who lived in a six-up six-down two streets
away. No problem, and that way I got the lamb scraps and my
rent reduced. The tenants usually had the rent and if they didn't
they'd have it the next week. If I was short I could use their rents
and pay next week too, which helped me. In the daytime I was
working as a bookmaker's assistant for the Sesame chain, taking
money and stamping times on slips, but the pay was lousy.
Sometimes I did the board but because I was new to it I had to
listen hard to get the prices right. I was a fill-in, which meant I
travelled all over the city to wherever someone was off sick. On
Narcissus Hill a man put two thousand on a dog each afternoon
race. In Cement Lane the windows were bullet-proof. In Cherub
Winchington a man punched the manager. I made more on travel
expenses than I did from the part-time pay.

While I was collecting the rents I discovered some
information about one of the tenants in the house two streets
away. Gerald Maloney; I knew his name from the mail that was
always clipped neatly under the bent metal flap of his spy-hole.
All the rooms had spy-holes. A certain Greek Mafioso syndicate
operated in the area and Costas, the restaurateur and my
landlord, had been involved in providing accommodation for low-
level knee-breaker members. When the Department of

Gerald at the Colonic Club

Environment closed down the Shishkabooty Kebab Hut things calmed down and now the house was rented to a regular tenancy. I met Gerald in the dining room one afternoon pouring dry spaghetti into dry mincemeat for the next day's meal and we exchanged pleasantries on the convenience of batch-baking. I noticed his shy New Zealand accent, and it would've been negligent not to notice his tall, thin frame and blond features. He stooped slightly and wore easy backpacking wear – long, shiny Lycra shorts, denim shirt, running shoes. He was following the pink continents of a world map with his finger as I passed through. I told him of my job and my plans to move into bookmaking management at which he disappeared and returned with a portable word processor that looked very much like a typewriter. Gerald told me I could write to some people and get a job if I'd like to borrow this processor. He went off to install the telecommunications systems of his current post and I sat down with the machine until curiosity led me straight to the personal files of its owner.

Gerald Maloney – born Christchurch, New Zealand, 1960 – had unsuccessfully attempted to join a monastery. The six or seven pages of his resumé listed all the subjects that he'd ever learnt in various institutions around the world. These included research groundwork for a sociology thesis into an observed trend for people to use their left hands to reach for loose coinage from their pockets and handbags, and half a year learning creative writing in Auckland. Gerald now worked in the city as a telephone systems installer but he obviously had plans for better things.

In the list of files I chanced upon a short story about a man called Joe who had got religion from a girl called Beth and ended up sad and lonely. It was called 'Joe's Story'. I read two or three pages, then went to 'Letter to Sandy'. The machine had a long, green oblong screen above the keyboard and the user processed words onto this screen. When the document was ready, paper was fed in as with a typewriter and the machine printed. Sandy'd been sent her letter the year before and it seemed that Joe'd been abandoned some time before that.

I would have printed it for my own reference had the ribbon not dried, but the letter to Sandra went something like this:

Cher Sandra,

Firstly CONGRATULATIONS ON YOUR
ENGAGEMENT AND I WISH YOU MANY
GOOD THINGS AND HAPPINESS. I HOPE
THAT YOU WILL BE VERY HAPPY.

I heard that you were in London recently. It was
about the time that Katharine and I were going
through the death throes of our relationship. I had
just lost my job and couldn't bear to be with her any
more and she couldn't bear to be with me either and
I guess that at the end we just didn't love each other
enough to want to stay together and make it work.
We'd talked of marriage and were even going to
spend our honeymoon on a canal boat over here. It's
taken me a long time to feel like myself again. Six
years' living together. It was not a good time.

As you know the monastery I applied to was full.
I spent a day in a Buddhist monastery when I was
researching for my sociology and religion thesis and
I liked it.

You heard from JD. I didn't think he would marry
that girlfriend. I thought he wasn't ambitious enough
for her. She certainly had him around her little finger.
I ran into JD in New York. We did some painting and
decorating for $20 an hour but somehow Peggy
wangled it so that he got $12 and I got $8 because he
was qualified. I thought that was tight and I wouldn't
stitch a friend in New York or anywhere. He was going
to go to New Jersey to do more. I came on over here.

Mother says I have a letter waiting for me from
Debbie Saltrow. She's married. I can't imagine her
married. I didn't think she'd do that. It will be good
to hear from her.

I'm seeing a rich American woman at the moment.
She's called Willma Carling. I sip champagne with her
on the deck of her boat. She took me to an exclusive
club called the Colonic which is invitation only. I'd
heard about it and always wanted go. It's full of

writers and film-makers. Willma should be taking me
to some other exclusive clubs.

I'm on a course of anti-depressants. I'm not
depressed but in America half the population are on
Prozac and it's supposed to get you motivated and
make you feel good about things. I went to my
doctor and said I'd gone on a course in NZ and so he
just signed the prescription. That's what doctors
want to hear. They don't want to think for
themselves, they just want you to tell them what to
prescribe. It's a month long course, and it's been
three weeks but I don't feel motivated. I don't feel
like doing anything. I just sit and watch these game
shows they have over here.

I hope you make it over again. Write soon.

Gerald

So Gerald had been at the Colonic Club. Like most people I was
best acquainted with the Colonic through the pages of the daily
press. It was the sort of place you might see pictured in *The
Assertive Gryphon* because it's bought a piece of shock artwork for
above the cash register. It had an impressive list of celebrity
members who turned up to be turned away at the whim of the
proprietor, an eccentric woman called Bibby Jean, who had run a
similar club in Burma in the 1950s. Photos showed the club as a
small bar-room with old, unspectacular furniture and woodchip
wallpaper that years of nicotine had turned a thick cream colour.
If you looked closely you could spot two or three small round
tables on ironwork bases set with heavy china ashtrays and plastic
baskets of snacks. Sharper eyes found corner-curled postcards of
Cuba and Paraguay pinned to wood surround. And that the bar
itself had a small optic range of expensive malt whiskies –
Glenlyric, Strathloman Fine – and one each of regular spirits
apart from vodka. The proprietor's anti-Russian feeling was well-
documented in the dailies. The precise reason why was hard to
ascertain since she wouldn't talk to the press or allow them access
to the Colonic when 'on-duty'. But it was generally known that
she'd been spurned in teen love by a Russian sailor who couldn't

speak the language and as a result she'd never married or stocked vodka in her club.

Further down on Gerald's menu was 'Willma Carling, Woman of Art', a short story of a New York artist promoter who'd come to London and taken a boat on the Thames to exhibit works by young British artists. Things had lapsed in the promoter's plans when she couldn't get a drinks license for her gallery but, determined not to give up, she had met a young New Zealand boy in the foyer of a fourteen-screen cinema multiplex near the city's Chinese quarter. Then the promoter had seduced this boy, young Jeremy of stock-hand background, and they'd made love aboard her boat to the happy rhythm of the incoming tide. The story went on to describe the rocketing love affair. There was an unexplained incident involving a floating disco boat. The story was very much like 'Joe's Story': nothing happened and I was disappointed.

Then there was a short letter to Mrs Maloney.

Dear Mother,
Letting you know things are all well over here. I have the same girlfriend. Hope to be changing jobs soon now. Willma knows a television scriptwriter who writes the farming soap opera they have over here, like Watunga Ranch. She says she can get me a trial with him. He's called Dewey Chinn. He's from a little town called Stourbridge and he has a strange accent. I still haven't been able to get in touch with Myrtle. I guess she's not there much. You told her I was here. She's old, she must be at home some time. I'll keep trying. Love to Dad and Rhoda.
Your son
Gerald

There were no other files on the machine. I thought that I might borrow it again some time in the future and in the meantime watch out for Gerald, admire his machine, confess a love of letter writing and encourage him to write letters home to friends and neighbours in New Zealand.

Gerald at the Colonic Club

The next week I found Gerald at the kitchen sink with the plastic baskets out from his fridge. He was having a spring clean. I'd seen the inside of Gerald's room and he did not have much in the way of personal items but he was clean. He was saving all his money for his big trip: Indo-China by bicycle or Africa on foot. I commented how much better I felt for a letter home to a loved one.

'Ever heard of the Colonic Club?' I asked as he used his finger to scrape green film from the lip of one of the baskets.

'I've been there,' he replied.

'No! What's it like, then?'

'Bunch of old men getting pissed.'

'Really? But is it good?'

'Yeah.'

'Who goes there?'

'Gregory Bertrand. You know, the one-armed writer, he's only got one arm.'

'Wow! How did he lose that arm?'

'Rotivator accident. Electricity surge. I've seen the stump.'

'Really? Who else?'

'Davy Hirsch.'

'Oh wow.'

'Yeah. They've got one of his paintings in there. From his blindfold phase. Willma displays him.'

'Who's Willma?'

'She's my girlfriend. She's from New York.'

'So do you want to become a member?'

'Yeah.'

'Don't you have to be a celebrity or famous for something?'

'I'm a writer. I might be writing for Elmskerdale soon.'

'Really?'

'Yeah. I think they need someone to get Katy's character out of submission with the butcher. They want him out. The raw chicken stinks up the studio.'

'Really?'

'Yeah.'

I left it there.

The next week I was ushering at the wedding of Costas's

daughter to the son of a cottons trader so I left the rents for that week. My job was to park the cars along the yellow lines of the main street so the bride could get out directly outside the restaurant. The previous evening I'd helped with sashing up the cars and restaurant front with cut-price satin bandeaux from the groom's side. Costas had taken down the front of the restaurant so that guests could walk in straight off the street. I hung around for a couple of souvlakis and chatted with the groom's mother, who spoke reasonable English. As I left, the couple were doing the money dance where guests pin money to the newly-weds instead of buying presents. You could get away with giving ten pounds in the flurry but Costas's family was generous and the cotton-trader's son was coated in a chain of fifties. I nipped along the two streets and punched the door combination of the rented house to find Gerald fixing a bicycle in the corridor. He'd got oil on his shorts from oiling the chains, so he stopped and sat down.

'Dirty job,' I said.

'Yeah,' said Gerald. 'I'll have to shower.'

'Going anywhere special?'

'Willma's boat. She's got a Davy Hirsch installation opening in the gallery. Stuff from his hands-tied period. He stands in front of his subject and paints with his hands tied behind his back. She was lucky to get him. It's a big night.'

'Wow.'

'Yeah. Then on for steam pudding and Glenlyric at the Colonic.'

'Steam pudding?'

'It's traditional on St John Caulfield's birthday. They gave him banana and custard one year and there was trouble or so Jack Julius told me. Apparently St John Caulfield reviews so much food he never gets time for the stuff he really likes, the nursery stuff. They'll all be there. Nigel Walker.'

'*Daily Organ?*'

'Yeah, and Davy Hirsch's mate Joel from Stretch.'

'What, they let pop stars in?'

'Yeah. Couple of children's TV presenters. I've met most of them before. Jack Julius. Nelson Id.'

'I've been reading some Nelson Id. He's good. I got a limited edition spiral-bound copy of *Dire Straitjackets* from the bookshop.'

'I've got that too. There's a misprint on page nineteen but it's only in the first twenty thousand. Who else? Harry Helium. Talks very fast and high about politics. Been on TV. Gordon and Bonnie Viva. Gregory Bertrand. Norma Bachelor, the superb model. Other superb models. '

'Yeah?'

'Cassandra Spritzer, American superb model. Leona Begonia, TV comedienne, dresses up as a dead person. Got her own chat show. She's new. Your sense of humour's weird over here.'

'I don't like St John Caulfield. He never goes out to enjoy a meal. He just goes to pick holes. He killed Cinque Twenty-Seven, not that I ever went but I read about it.'

'Yeah. Writes from his health club in the country but never gets any thinner. Is that a British thing?'

'Could be.'

He told me that he was following the Great British Cycle Race, starting in Edinburgh in two months' time. Gerald was, as it turned out, a cycling enthusiast and he had at least two bicycles in the back which he kept oiled for the weekend. I told him I'd had some positive responses to my letters of the week before, and he left me the keys to his room so I could use the word processor again.

My attention was immediately drawn to 'Letter to JD'.

Dear JD,

Hey, you old bastard. It's me Gerald in old England. I'm having a gay old time of it here, let me tell you. How's the wife? Any regrets? Sorry I couldn't get out for the wedding. I got a letter from Sandra and she told me the news. I expect you thought I'd be back home by now. I've decided to stay on a while. I've got a serious girlfriend, who is from New York, you may have seen her – ha! – and things are going pretty well. I was a bit depressed last year but I took Prozac for a while and felt good again. Good advice from you, JD! I guess I must've remembered what you were like when you were wallpapering, knowing all the questions on the radio phone-ins. They don't really have that thing over here in the same way. There is a station called Freak FM which comes on for six hours a day from a tenement flat in the eastern part of the city with a young black guy called Groovy D who says, 'Yo going out to De-li-la in the Ce-ment Lane Laund-er-ette,' over drum and bass music which sounds like a bunch of mosquitoes.

I stopped reading to note Gerald's familiarity with youth culture and the marked upturn in his mood due, I suspected, to the Prozac.

You'd like Willma, JD. She really moves with it. She's older than me – forty-four – and she's obese but it's funny because Willma can wear a pink furry catsuit and be seventeen stone and still look good. It's the way she holds herself. And the art kids love her. She's got this installation on her yacht of some stuff that's opening this week. It's by Davy Hirsch. Have you heard of him? He was pictured naked on a zebra on the cover of *Tick Tock*. Him and Willma were both painted up like an African scene. Apparently, according to Willma, he did all the painting himself, even his back and tush. That's a Willma word. Tush. She shakes her big tushie for me on the captain's bunk.

Willma takes me to this British club called the Colonic where you get spotted dick. Don't ask me, but it's some kind of dessert. The Colonic's this crazy cat club upstairs from a baker's in Chinatown. It's like a back room. Everyone stands. There are tables but everyone stands. It's run by this woman called Bibby Jean and she decides whether she likes you or not and if she doesn't you can't come in. Willma said she doesn't think either way about me so that must be good.

Gerald at the Colonic Club

To sign in you don't write your name. Bibby Jean gives you this character in history and you have to sign in with that. Then when someone comes up to you and asks you who you are, you can be you or the historical celebrity. I'm Captain Oates. Every time I go to the men's room I say, 'I might be a while.' Willma loves it. Willma's Cleopatra. Davy Hirsch is Jason the Argonaut. There's this famous writer called Nelson Id. Everyone talks about him. He's been institutionalized and he formed an addiction to bleach while he was in this strange place on the moorland somewhere and so his mouth is deformed. He does this stuff about madness and all that. He's Winston Churchill. He made me guess him one time when I was queueing for the men's room. I got him after twenty-three. I thought he might be Groucho Marx with the cigar until he went on about the beaches.

JD, the Colonic's an experience you would enjoy, my Kiwi friend. Entrance is through an iron door in the street and then you're outside again. You can see bread coming out of the ovens and ducks on poles where the baker's baking for the Chinese restaurant next door so you get this strange smell of roast meat and new dough cooking. The john's right opposite so you normally get a really strong smell from there too. There's this food writer called St John Caulfield and he goes in with *The Daily Organ* and writes letters on the crapper to the editor. He works for *The Assertive Gryphon* but he writes letters to the *Organ* under pseudonyms to see if they get printed. Willma says she pees in the yard behind when Caulfield's just vacated, which means she's got to get out of her furry catsuit.

Sex with Willma is amazing. She buys these rubber toys and masks and sticks pins in my hind and I love it. We've had it in the Colonic john. She's a very athletic lady. She did a gymnastic position over the bowl and I did it from above. It's not like it was with Katharine once a week with the lights on. Willma's at it all the time. She can't leave me alone. We'll be in a cab and she's got down and she's giving me a mouth job. You know, JD, I think this could be it. We're made for each other. I used to think I was dull but Willma's got me shagging all over the city. That's British – shagging. Willma and I shagged on a water bed in the Bed Surgery. I guess shagging is just sex when you don't care. I got it from a children's TV presenter. I got penile warts from Willma at the beginning. Ever had penile warts, JD? Christ, I was low and I had to go and get my stoker out on a table for a woman doctor. It was very embarrassing. You always did bring out the worst in me, JD.

Got to go now. Write soon, you old dog.

Gerald M.

I readjusted my position on the raffia two-seater sofa in the communal sitting room and moved the cursor down the green oblong screen.

Dear Willma,

I guess you don't expect your NZ toyboy to write to you. You said last night that it was good having me around and it's good to be around but I guess I'm used to more commitment in a relationship. You know that Katharine and I lived together and for me it was hard to get over it in this country but then I met you and you took me to some great places and I kind of got used to you and me.

What is Davy in all of this? He's always there. Are you two dating? Am I in the way? Tell me. I felt funny the other night when he showed with Nelson. Are those two guys just friends or what? Does he like you? Let me know. I want you to come to NZ with me. I've told my friends and folks about you. I've written a short story about you, Willma. I want to

Gerald at the Colonic Club

show it to Dewey Chinn. When's he going to show?
I can't wait to see you and have you read it.
Scalding Shaft

I decided I would have to penetrate Gerald's mail.

It was very hot in the summer of 1996 and my windowless back room began to smell. Some years before, the room had served as a slaughter chamber where young pigs and cattle were brought in on ropes to be slaughtered and hung. Costas had developed most of his regular clientele from this traditional way of food creation but, as one of the last Greek in-house slaughterers in the area, he eventually had to bow to public pressure and buy in frozen. The room was carpeted and painted dark green now; perhaps the smell was my imagination. It was hard to imagine bloody carcass piles where the portable bar now stood or trays of hearts and livers on the shelves now weighted down with my weekend interest – hospital lab foetuses and appendices.

When I wasn't travelling to one of the bookmaker's shops in a different area, I spent my time on the streets, often brushing down the restaurant pavement. Once a week, Costas gave me the keys to his car and I went to the supermarket to pick up lettuces and salad vegetables for the kebab menu. Costas's car was a convertible Mercedes. Although it was up-to-date, it was the sort of car Barbie and Ken might have driven in the 1970s. It had pale pink metallic bodywork – Costas's choice of respray – and a deep red roll-off roof. It had a stainless steel dashboard, and the pink pigskin upholstery had been custom-made by an Italian interior trimmer. The eight-track stereo was from Costas's first British car, a Ford Anglia, and it had four buttons for the different tracks, each decorated with a psychedelic swirl pattern.

The supermarket was about a mile and a half away and I often went around the one-way system several times to enjoy the ease of steering and the envious glances from bus stop queues. A long-term diversion in Bold Newington meant that traffic was often static and I had to be careful to dress suitably so as to perpetuate the notion that it was my car. And one day, driving up Bold Newington High Street, I noted a strange thing.

It was the hottest day of the season so far and in bare feet you would've noticed the tarmac nearly bubbling. Along the road the traffic stopped and started around deliveries of water melons. Lithe young men swung their way out of red vans, naked but for shorts, melon-slice T-shirts and huge gloves. Ahead along the lines of cars you could see a brown arm hanging limply from every driver's window. Brown hands clipped fingernails on the sides and roofs of the cars, waggling wing mirrors, lighting cigarettes with hot-to-touch lighters, running fingers through sweat-soaked hair. The cars sizzled in the dry, close heat and on the pavements pedestrians shuffled about like thirsty unclipped poodles.

With my foot weakly jammed on the clutch, as I came abreast with the boarded-up Underworld American Coffee House, I stopped to look to my left. A man in a business suit had stepped out of his car on to the road and he was taking off his jacket. His shirt was damp and he knelt into the car to put the jacket around the back of the driver's seat as if the seat were wearing it. The man looked familiar; in his forties, you could tell, but he looked younger, very carefully younger. He had a boyish thrust about him. As he stood by his low silver car, he calmed it to bay with brisk wrist-flicks as he loosened his tie and folded it on to the passenger seat. I watched and felt his relief as he undid the buttons of his shirt and took off that too. And then his vest and trousers. When he was down to his socks and Y-fronts, he caught up his ankles one by one and tore off the socks, rolled down the pants and stood naked by the car. I knew this man. Or at least I knew his face. He was in *The Assertive Gryphon* once a week. It was Jack Julius, ironic columnist and ghost-writer of top celebrity autobiographies. But what was he doing naked in Bold Newington High Street?

Jack Julius knelt down on the road, which must have stung his knees, and started praying. He put his hands together and prayed, looking up at the sky and squinting. Shortly afterwards a policewoman from the police station some yards up the street appeared and took the jacket from the back of the seat and put it around Julius. She helped him into his car and the traffic was stopped while she U-turned the car and drove it against the traffic back to the station. Then I drove on.

I waited a few days to visit Gerald again with my bright red spiral-bound book of dates and pound signs. I passed through the security door and found him using wet and dry sandpaper on the rusty spokes of his second-choice bicycle. He was strenuously rubbing the narrow poles up and down and his hands had gone a copper colour. Flecks of copper-coloured liquid were forming on his shins. He lifted his sweaty head and passed me his keys and I went through to his room. Several letters were balanced on the inexpensive wood cabinet that held Gerald's anti-perspirants, but I chose one. A parchment billet-doux in a firm businesslike hand headed 'Willma Carling, Agent to Modernists:

> Dear Scalding Shaft,
>   How strange for you to write to me, baby! You know how much I like my Scalding Shaft in the mornings. And just when I'd bought the two-stroke anal stoker. Davy and I are friends, you know that. You mustn't be jealous. Get it out of your system, Scalding, and come to see me on Friday evening with your satchel and sneakers.
>   Willma

Hurriedly I replaced the letter in its long beige envelope and reached to the top of the wardrobe for the processor.

'I saw Jack Julius reach the end of his tether in the high street,' I said to Gerald as I came back through. 'Any idea why?'

'Me? No. Uh. He just lost it. Got too hot. And there happened to be an Organ photographer in one of the cars behind.'

'Have you seen him since?'

'No. He hasn't been around and about the, uh, places I go.'

'Oh. And how's Willma?'

'Yeah. Great. We're in love. I'm off to see her soon.'

'Great.'

'Yeah.'

'Any news on your membership yet?'

'Should be soon. They're reading my *Elmskerdale* script and it's looking good. The butcher gets caught peddling soft drugs to *Elmskerdale* schoolkids by Mrs Endymion. He hides them in the dripping and she gets half a pound by mistake off Katy who's

developed vertigo dementia now they live above the shop.'
'Really? I collect hospital specimens myself. You know, diseased bladders, tumours, malformations.'
'Really?'
'Yeah.'
I left it there.

I would've liked to have thought that I read *The Assertive Gryphon* cover to cover every day but in truth I invariably picked up *The Daily Organ* from the restaurant kitchen and flipped through it for my horoscope.

It was with surprise, therefore, that I picked up the paper the next week to read that a curious case of 'spontaneous implosion' had taken place in countryside outside Remnants Heath. And I was even more surprised to read that the incident, the like of which had been unseen since 1848, involved none other than St John Caulfield. Startled, I read on as police officers came on to the scene and found a peculiar picture poolside at the Christie Lido Health Spa. 'It was as if a human balloon had burst on the patio slabs,' ran the distressed quotation from manager Friedrich Sel.

Under the headline 'HONEST ST JOHN IN HEALTH FARM HORROR', confused reports had Caulfield variously napping after lunch, relaxing in a massage session, on the telephone to his editor and dangling his feet in the water. The colour photograph showed a stark scene of steak-like fragments covering the diving area of a wave-machine Hawaiian lido. Restaurant staff said that Caulfield had eaten lunch as usual and that he appeared well. Mr Sel commented that the deceased was a pleasant gentleman and that every year he gave staff a Christmas box. For some reason, my mind jumped to Gerald and Willma and suddenly all I could think was that Willma wouldn't need to take off her pink furry catsuit round the back of the bakery any more.

Gerald had written to Debbie Saltrow.

Dear Debbie,
Good to hear from you. Mother forwarded your letter. So you're married! I always knew you would get married before me. Remember Katharine? We're not together any more. She said I got too heavy. Does

that sound like me?! You know it's worked in my favour. I'm becoming quite a success over here in England. I'm writing for this countryside soap opera and it's really taking off. It's a drama, set in this nuclear basin called Elmskerdale but it's not like the country in NZ. There's a bombing, there are murders, lesbians, drugs. It's great. I'm scripting out to new young writers all the time. Come on over. I'll give you a job! Forget that creative writing shite. That's an English word – shite. The pop stars say it for shit. There are two brothers, Ian and Joel, from a band called Stretch. They have an album called *Shite Tomorrow And Every Day After*. They're members of my club. My club! It's called the Colonic. I go once a week and meet friends. My girlfriend Bibby Jean runs it. She's older than me by twenty-five years but she can still go some.

Mother said you have kids. Great! I hear it's painful. Not for me. Bibby Jean's too old. We could adopt. Several of the writers that come in have illegitimate children and we could just get one of them. I know you'd like Nelson Id. He comes in. He's my mate! I'll send you his new stories. I can't stay any more. I'm going to get my new computer and I'm moving house and it's all happening. Love to mother if you see her.

Gerald

Gerald was on the move. I had one last week's rent to collect and there was a letter in Willma's businesslike hand clipped to the spyhole. I had wondered about Willma in all of this. Had she bored of Gerald or had he bored of her? The envelope was sealed in a businesslike way that meant it could easily be opened and resealed so I took my place for the last time on the raffia two-seater. It was the last time for me because Costas had offered me management of a new kebab booth in the financial area of the city. Costas knew how to predict a successful trend and kebabs for lunch after trading all morning on the money markets was one of them.

Gerald,
What do you think you are doing with Bibby Jean
Boothroyd? I introduced her to you. She thinks
you're nothing more than an Australian rough-neck.
She told me so. How could you be so sly and
disingenuous as to go off with my best friend after
everything you said to me about commitment and
you and your wretched Katharine. You've let me
down, Gerald. Bibby Jean's a harridan. Well, don't
forget people burn in this city and your turn will
come. I'm from New York. I burnt out while you
were still dirtying your diapers. I know the game and
you're playing it. Bibby Jean doesn't love you. She's a
fickle old hag and she'll have you out of the Colonic
as soon as she's bored. Your trunks are in the trash.
The men come on Monday, so if you want them
come and get them out.
Willma Carling
Agent to Modernists

Gerald gave me a fifty-pound tip for taking his rent for the
summer. I spent the money on a carcinogenic kidney and a couple
of bloated lungs from the incurable disease department at St
Giles's. Later, I often saw Gerald from my kebab booth. In fact, I
served him with a large chicken shish but he didn't recognize me.
He was with a young superb model called Honey Fairchild.
Gerald was always in the magazines with the superb models or at
the Colonic with the writers and the pop stars. He had put on
weight with his incidental food columns for *The Assertive Gryphon*.
He was writing for the top soap opera *Way Down in Weybridge* but
it was coming round to summertime again and it was getting
hotter and hotter and it felt like someone was going to burn.

Elisabeth Sheffield
The Dairy Queen

– We really need to rest now, Mrs Karetski.

No doubt about it – because she's been talking nonstop for the last three hours, repeating the same stories about her travels to the Middle East, over and over. For surely before long this incessant chatter will create a lesion in her brain, as the same circuit of memory is activated again and again, a groove in the tissue like the path worn into the carpet by the customers at the Bank as one after another shuffles through the same series of transactions. And Oleta doesn't want that to happen, nor does she want to wear the skin off Mrs K's old back, the back she has been scrubbing and scrubbing with the loofah mitt, and which in the last hour, no matter how many times she rinses it, never ceases to yield a fresh crop of little grey pellets. Just a short while ago she warned her: Mrs K, we're going to rub you raw.

– Don't worry about it, honey, Mrs K had replied. – I've got a hide like a horse. Besides, I haven't had a good scrubbing since Ron and I went to the Turkish bath in Istanbul in 1972.

But her flesh is soft and crumbly as feta cheese and it is obvious to Oleta that she'll never reach some fresher, more fundamental layer. Clearly something must be done, but what? What would Jackie do? What *did* she do on those late nights of sailing the halcyon waters of the Mediterranean when Ari wanted to sit up on the deck and talk, or worse, and all she desired was sleep? Halcion, that's it. Oleta excuses herself and walks into the vast kitchen, ostensibly to fetch Mrs K a blood pressure pill and a small glass of water. She even goes so far as to open the vial of pills on the window ledge behind the porcelain sink, since Mrs

K's hearing remains surprisingly acute. Gazing out at Central Park, but not focusing, so that everything is a soft green blur because it's too early in the day, for God's sake, to witness a crime, she opens the vial. She opens it, closes it and taps her fingernail on the Formica counter to simulate the sound of a pill being placed there. Then, as she lets the water run from the tap so that it will be nice and cold, she quickly steps over to the kitchen table and takes a Halcion out of the little ivory pillbox in her purse.

Mrs K's bleary blue eyes and arthritic fingertips fail to detect that the sleeping pill is tiny, white and ovoid, unlike her blood pressure pills, which are larger, pink and disc-shaped. Which is just as well, even though the substitution is for her own good. Maybe Oleta could eventually convince her of the shameful truth that is slowly killing off America's senior citizens – that the doctors have conspired with the pharmaceutical companies to overdose the elderly – but it would take hours, hours which would only deprive Mrs K of the sleep she so desperately needs. Further, even if Oleta were able to persuade her to cut down or relinquish her present dosage of blood pressure pills, no doubt the authorities would eventually find out and undo her good deed. It is a terrible thing, Oleta thinks, the way the medical establishment callously stuffs old people like Mrs K with pills. Anyone who has observed the habits of elderly dogs and cats can see that Nature meant for aged bodies to rest.

Mrs K has swallowed the Halcion and is lifting the glass of water to her wrinkled lips for a second sip to wash it down when the phone rings. Oleta keeps a gentle and reassuring hand on her shoulder until she is finished drinking, and then she takes the glass from her and places it on the marble-topped table at the other end of the chaise lounge where she won't be able to knock it over and stain the silk damask. That way there'll be no need to re-upholster the piece after Mrs K dies, since the fabric is hardly worn. Anyway, no reason to rush since most likely it is that district attorney Oleta went home with from the Buffer Zone the other night, calling to say again that she looks just like her sister Leota, and that he's in love with her. She should never have given him the phone number at Mrs K's, but then we all sometimes lose our way in the fog of postcoital bliss.

The phone is at the far end of Mrs K's Upper East Side apartment, on the little marquetry nightstand with the carved Cupid pedestal next to her bed. Oleta picks up the receiver, her eyes coming to rest on a photo of Mrs K and her beloved Ron, with identical caps of silvery grey hair and matching pea-green sweat suits, standing on the banks of the Bosphorous. She expects to hear the lisp of her Buffer Zone lover but instead she is greeted by the huskier, although no less boyish, tones of her brother-in-law.

– I'm really sorry to bother you Oleta, I know how important your weekends with that old lady are to you, that it's not just a job but a vocation . . .

She gently interrupts. – Peter, what's the matter?

His words jumble forth like gumballs from a broken dispenser: it seems that he is worried about Leota, who was recently diagnosed with Lyme Disease. She's perpetually tired, weak as a kitten, and because the oral medication for the Lyme is not working, she now has to take it intravenously. At this point his voice begins to tremble – Leota needs help injecting the medication and he has a golf date this afternoon and, anyway, he can't stand the sight of blood.

In the photo on the nightstand, so beautifully preserved in a sterling silver, heart-shaped frame, Mr and Mrs K look like twins. Once Oleta mentioned this to Mrs K and she replied that people who pair early in life inevitably do – that not all twins are made in the womb. She and her Ronny had been two peas in a pod, even though he was twenty years older. Mrs K said this as if she were defending a strand of cultured pearls, which she'd admitted weren't the genuine article but were nevertheless of excellent quality. At that point Oleta told her that people tended to romanticize twinhood. Surprisingly, Mrs K had replied that people also idealize marriage and went on to confess that Ron could be difficult – that he'd been a womanizer and vain to boot. That last year, she told Oleta, he had insisted that he wanted a nanny, not a nurse because a nurse would make him feel like an old man. If it hadn't been for that damn incompetent nanny, she said, her eyes welling up with tears, her Ronny might have survived his last heart attack.

133

And if Mrs K weren't sound asleep, Oleta might tell her, after she gets off the phone, that there's a big difference between a burden voluntarily assumed and one assigned by genetics. Would Christ have been able to carry that cross up Calvary Hill so easily if he'd been born with it, if it had been made of bone instead of wood and rooted in his spine? The truth is that Leota has been a thorn in Oleta's flesh ever since they were both in the womb, or maybe siphon would be more accurate, as Oleta emerged weighing only 5.2 pounds to Leota's 8.5. The doctor told their mother that it could have been worse – that she should be grateful to have borne *two* healthy identical twin girls, as he'd read of cases where one twin completely absorbed the other the only evidence afterwards of foetal foul play being a tiny pearl-like fingernail embedded in the flesh of the newborn's stomach or an odd swirl of hair on the palm of her hand.

The struggle in the womb continued on the outside, as a fight in a bar will spill onto the street. According to their mother, her breasts were a war zone, for as soon as Oleta would start nursing, Leota would inevitably plunge for the same teat. A battlefield from which Leota always emerged triumphant, for she would scream and cry until she'd gained the whole territory and only when she'd glutted herself on the spoils of her victory and had fallen back into a milky swoon would Oleta be allowed to take her share. As the twins grew, things only got worse. Oleta learnt not to talk aloud to herself in her crib because Leota would steal the words right out of her mouth. 'Diaper,' she'd say or 'whisky' when their mother finally came in to change and feed them, her pronunciation perfect after listening to Oleta practise all morning. Whatever Oleta achieved – honourable mention in a short story contest, a medal for saving a boy from drowning, the winning goal on the hockey team – Leota would take credit for it by leaping up onto the podium or thrusting herself in front of the camera, while Oleta would stand there with her mouth open, dumbfounded by yet another pre-emptive strike.

Oleta's pulse has accelerated. She is not counting but it is possible to discern the increased rate through a certain tingling in her wrists. It's no wonder: she had thought that Peter could take her place, that he would allow her to sever the mental and emotional bond that joins Leota to her as firmly as any junction of the flesh. That even if he stopped short of being Leota's psychic Siamese twin, he could provide her, like the rock that is his namesake, with some sort of foundation. Because Oleta is tired of supporting the arts. And to be sure, financially he is solid. No more need she worry about her sister siphoning off her savings, as she once sucked up her share of the placental sustenance. But unfortunately Leota requires more than financial stability and Oleta is beginning to fear that Peter is unsound. And if Peter cannot be relied upon, if Oleta cannot direct her full attention to what matters most to her, then she will never be able to realize her dream.

The other end of the line is silent but for the sound of Peter's breathing, which is both as light and as laboured as a sick child's. He is waiting, waiting for Oleta to say that she will take the next train to New Canaan.

– All right. I'm coming. But I'll need an extra bed for Mrs Karetski.

Mrs K, who woke up just outside the city, is sitting hunched in the corner of the seat opposite Oleta's, shivering in the folds of her gold appliqued sweat suit even though the train's air conditioning is not working.

– Where are we going? she demands. – Why did you take me away from my home? Are you going to kidnap me?

Oleta leans forward and takes Mrs K's hand. In a grave voice, she explains to her that they're on their way to visit Mrs K's husband, who is not really dead. She goes on to say that he has been in a federal witness protection programme since 1982, hiding from his enemies in organized crime – a not entirely implausible story since she knows that the Queens steak house franchise where Ron Karetski supposedly made his fortune was really a front for a chop shop chain.

And Mrs K apparently knows this as well because she doesn't say another word. But Oleta can see from her wildly dilated blue eyes that her mind is dancing with visions of her dead sugar daddy, and this gives Oleta the deepest satisfaction. For the old need their imaginations stimulated as much as the young, she thinks. In fact, such mental kindling may be more important in the second childhood than in the first, for the child's mind can grasp at the slightest straw and make it into a raft for the imagination to sail away on. But in the elderly mind, the same straw is sucked into the languorous vortex of senility, obliterated in the slowly whirling circuit of memory replayed again and again and again.

Oleta's theorizing is interrupted by a shriek. She looks over and sees a Barbie camper hanging by two wheels from the seat tray of the little girl across the aisle. Two identical blond Barbies are falling through the open windshield, their nylon locks spilling out onto the hood as the girl cries:

– Ruth, I never should've let you drive!

Clearly this is going to end in tragedy. Oleta averts her eyes as the camper plummets into the aisle and the little girl begins to wail.

Suddenly she finds herself thinking of Richard. She thought she had closed the coffin of that memory years ago but somehow it starts to seep out from under the lid. Richard. Mom called him 'Rich' and told them to be extra good when he came over. After a long line of grifters and graduate students in dacron-blend chinos and grungy dungarees, he seemed eminently suitable in his expensive suits that were always tailored in some fine woollen fabric, with a silk handkerchief peeking out of the jacket pocket. Furthermore, he drove a Saab not a rusted Pinto or a Maverick.

The Saturday morning after the first night Richard stayed over at their house, he had promised that he would come back in the afternoon and take the girls out for a 'treat'. They spent the rest of the morning, after he drove away in his black Saab, watching cartoons. For once Oleta didn't have to fight with Leota for the right to watch *UnderDog*. They watched the flying canine in perfect, non-hierarchical harmony, since their real interest that morning was in the commercials. Side by side, they gorged upon images of Easy-Bake Ovens, PF Flyers, Chatty Cathys, Silly String, Super Skates and even Rock-em Sock-em Robots, stuffing their imaginations with the objects that would soon overflow their toy boxes as they waited for Rich to return.

Their mother had dressed them in their city dresses – Oleta's was black above, white below, with big white plastic rings joining the tank top to the tube skirt, while Leota's was the reverse – and pulled their curly blond hair back in cascading ponytails that reached the smalls of their backs. When she was done, they had stared at each other, unable to pull apart as if trapped by the gravity of their mutual desire.

– My, don't you two look sexy? Mom had said, breaking the spell by giving them little pats on the bottom. – How could anyone resist you?

But resist them he did as he turned not in the direction of Manhattan and FAO Schwartz but on to the fast-food strip, which Mom, who was on the zoning committee, had helped to banish to the outskirts of their little upstate town. Past the hamburger joints, the pizza places and the taco stand, which studded the sides of the highway like neon flies, feeding on the lowly tastes of teenagers and truck drivers. At the very end, just before where the billboards began to give way to cornfields, he slowed down and turned the Saab into the parking lot of Dairy Queen.

Dutifully, Oleta ordered at the counter. Leota said she didn't want anything and sat slumped in the booth, arms crossed over her chest, while Richard slurped up a shake and Oleta ate her sundae, trying to ignore the sour milk taste of the ice cream beneath the strawberry syrup. Then, just as Richard had blotted the last bit of vanilla up off his gray flannels, and was standing up to go, Leota said:

– You know, *Dick*, maybe I will have a cone after all.

In the car, Oleta noticed that her sister only licked up the drops of melted cream that threatened to dribble over the edges. She wasn't actually eating her double dip and, sure enough, they'd been driving for less than five minutes when she let the cone plop to the floor. Richard, smiling into the rearview mirror, remarked:

– Ate that right up, didn't you?

Leota didn't answer but merely caught Richard's eyes in the mirror and grinned back. Silence, as Richard turned his attention back to the road and his own thoughts. Silence as Oleta sat there gazing at the blobs of orange and chocolate melting into the beige carpeting. And then she realized that Leota was muttering something: *ice cream, ice cream*. A mutter like a chant, as if she were urging it to melt, mouthing a spell to ooze deep into the nylon pile, to stick and glue, clump and gum. But how could Oleta know, how should she know what was coming? The fact that the eyes that had met Richard's in the rearview mirror minutes before were identical to her own, cornflower blue and slightly bulging, doesn't mean that the thoughts behind them were the same as well. Poor Richard. If only he'd been more alert. If he hadn't been so deeply into himself when Leota screamed the loudest, most piercing scream imaginable into his ear, maybe he wouldn't have been so completely jolted out.

Oleta doesn't think her sister intended to kill him, or even to cause a wreck. After all, they could easily have died as well if Richard hadn't insisted that they wear their seatbelts and strapped them in himself. The collision with the oncoming TV repair van was just an accident, and no one ever asked why there was ice cream melted into the backseat carpet. Still, the next morning after church when she saw the photo in the newspaper, over the caption, 'Twins survive double date with Death,' she wasn't exactly thrilled. While she'd been wanting her picture in the paper, she had envisioned different circumstances – had seen herself aloft on a float, a crown on her head and a banner across her chest, not standing next to a crumpled car, soiled with blood and dirt.

She'd stared at that picture, stared at the bloody handprint like the mark of Cain on her white tube skirt, until it had seemed as if there was a tiny red hand floating on the edge of her vision, frail and insistent as a gnat. A gnat, which she tried to dodge by skipping from column to column, leaping from one page to the next, from the front page to the sports section and back again. And then she saw her, in the centre of the people page, and for a moment there was nothing else – no Leota, no Richard, no gnat. Nothing but her big black sunglasses, her mysterious smile and the aura that protected her like mosquito netting from all the world's pricks and stabs. For a long moment Oleta just looked and then slowly, slowly inchoate desire took shape and burst like a chrysalis into consciousness: I wanna be like her.

The little girl's wailing has died down to delicate, hiccuping sobs and Mrs K's papery eyelids are closed, though Oleta is not sure she is asleep. She decides to take advantage of this fragile silence to fix her face. As she studies her slightly protruding but striking blue eyes, her rather retroussé nose and intriguingly under-ripe lips in her compact mirror, she feels the usual discouragement. If only she could really fix her face, for years she has known that plastic surgery is the only solution. She snaps the compact shut and a little spray of powder flys up, soft as a sigh. If she could just shed the skin of her twinhood, maybe she could at last live the life she was born for, the cool and luminous existence of the social butterfly. Not that she wouldn't work. After all, Jackie had become an editor after Ari had died. And hadn't she seemed more enigmatic than ever, sitting in her office chair, manuscript in her lap, peering up over the tops of her reading glasses at the camera? Unfortunately, Oleta had not forseen how Leota would trammel her dream, again and again. The last assault had nearly broken its wings.

The police caught Leota just as she was giving change to the 100ist customer who had bought an ice-cream cone from her phony franchise. It was ingenious, really. Every day she'd put on a tie-dyed T-shirt, plait her hair into a long corn-silk blond braid, which she'd pull over the plastic fastener at the back of her black baseball cap, and pencil freckles on her nose. Then she'd take the train to Tarrytown and set her vending cart up right outside the station. She'd gotten every detail right: the illustration on each carton of the two boyhood pals, the carefully casual handwriting, the wacky flavours. The only irregularity was the Huckleberry Warhol. It was both her signature and a tribute to Andy's soup cans, she'd told Oleta when she went to bail her out of the slammer.

Oleta doesn't carry a lot of baggage – just a genuine Gucci bag that she bought from a man on Columbus Circle who gave her a discount for her baby blue eyes – but she must admit that it is rather heavy. Thus she doesn't hold Peter's quiet groan, as he hoists it into the back of the jeep, against him. He is an excellent brother-in-law, entitled to a long-suffering sigh, and she tries to tell him this with a gentle pat on his shoulder blade.

– A Land Rover! Mrs K cries as Peter opens the back door and guides her into the leather upholstered interior. Why I haven't been in one of these since Ronny and I went to Nepal in 1967. Boy, did he look sharp in that white hat.

On the narrow and sinuous road to New Canaan, Peter asks Oleta if she has read the news about Jackie. She watches how the sunlight falling through the trees ripples the dark hood of the jeep with scales of light and slowly nods her head. Warm tears of gratitude begin to spill from her eyes. For surely Jackie had realized that her reign was coming to an end, had sensed like an ageing Dali Lama that the cosmic wheel was spinning and that her successor's number would soon come up. And now, wherever Jackie is, she knows that Oleta will soon be able to afford the operation and, further, that in another year or two, when Mrs K dies, she will come into her fortune. She knows, Oleta thinks as the tears rain down into her cupped hands, and has given me her blessing.

– I'm sorry, Oleta, Peter says. – I know how you feel.

Maybe he does, maybe he doesn't. The important thing is that he appears as if he does. She appreciated this about him – his uncannily Kennedy-like ability to look genuine – the first time she saw him at the Bank, sitting behind his big mahogany desk. He was reading the screen of his laptop (later she learnt that he'd been playing a video game), as she entered the room. She cleared her throat and he'd looked at her over the tops of his designer wire rims – given her a glance that combined the kindly, far-sighted welcome of a grandfather with the sexy come-hither of a con artist. A man that other men could trust, not because he was one – for such men are the most untrustworthy of all – but because he *looked* like one. Instantly Oleta knew he was right for Leota. She knew just as she did the time she spotted that navy floral sundress at Daffy's – that the fit would be perfect.

Of course it took Leota a while to recognize how well he suited her, just as she didn't immediately see that the navy of the sundress slimmed her hips while the scallops that bordered the open back not only lent her shoulder blades a certain delicacy, but even the possibility of downy feathers. No, she didn't appreciate that sundress at all when Oleta first gave it to her. It was hideous, she said. Like something a rich housewife from Connecticut would wear.

Admittedly, she was a bit miffed – especially since she'd thought the dress charming. But Leota came around: a year after she bought her the sundress, ten months after she introduced her to Peter, Leota had worn it to host a July Fourth barbecue at her brand-new eighteenth-century farmhouse in the Constitution State. And Oleta's pleasure at the sight of her in it was not diminished by Leota's insistence that it was a costume, meant, like the grilled soydogs, fresh-baked mock apple pie and quivering red, white and blue Jello mould shaped like America, to be taken completely ironically.

Because one cannot live on irony alone. Oleta witnessed this on the opening night of *I Scream, You Scream*, when Leota had swathed her body in swatches of old polyester and then stationed herself outside the entrance of the gallery, huddling in the shadows with a shopping bag full of old *New York Times*. Three, four, maybe five people came and went in the course of three hours, all of them women in thriftshop rags like Oleta's own, only hers were the real McCoy while theirs were Barney's forgeries. Alas, only a mere handful of spectators came to view the video recording of months of the most dedicated chicanery. Just a small band of undernourished and overeducated women with dirty hair and expensive underwear to sneer at what Leota had described in the programme brochure as a 'Quotation of Corporate America'. Oleta had actually heard one of them say, as she climbed down the fire escape with her companion, their matching jewelled cat-eye glasses sparkling in the streetlight, doesn't she know that the simulacrum is a cliché?

Now Peter is slowing down, gently guiding the Land Rover into the driveway. He brings it to a stop just before the car port, since there's no point in storing the jeep inside when he's going to be loading it up with golf gear in less than an hour.

Peter sets Oleta and Mrs K's bags down at the foot of the flagstone path that leads up to the front door, explaining that before they go inside Oleta has to see the new extension in the back.

– I bet you can't even tell where the genuine wood ends and

the Durasiding begins, he says, as Oleta admires the exterior of the new family room, which has sliding glass doors and a full length deck that looks out onto the lawn.

– Will I see my dear Ronny soon? Mrs K asks.

Oleta leans back against the deck railing and gazes at the fine green slope that rises up gradually from the back of the house. A ridiculously pink clump of peonies protrudes from the centre of the lawn and she thinks that if she lived here she'd have them uprooted. But Mrs K is tugging at her sleeve and so Oleta explains, winking first at Peter, that she doesn't know if Mrs K will see *her* deer, but it is quite likely that she will see *a* deer since they're quite common in suburban Connecticut.

Oleta chooses to ignore the frown on Mrs K's face as they walk back around to the front of the house, since it never does any good to indulge her sulks. On the porch, Peter sets their bags down again. With one hand on the brass knob of the glossy black door, he gestures with the other like a game show assistant, at the velvet sweep of lawn, at the dark perimeter of hemlocks and boxwood that screens his black-shuttered Dutch Colonial from view as elegantly as the widow's veil that hid Jackie's grief from the world's prying eyes. Oleta looks out at this fine piece of property and once more beams her approval at him. And indeed, Leota is very lucky to have all this – because she never stood the ghost of a chance of making it as an artist.

Apparently Leota finally realized this as well, since a few days after the failure of *I Scream, You Scream*, she had accepted Oleta's offer to arrange a dinner date for her with Peter. And, as Oleta had suspected, they immediately hit it off – like money and empty pockets, like tit for tat. She took him not just downtown but underground, to see basement acts of physical and mental abasement – a man locked up in a cage by his wife/sister/daughter, a woman obsessed with the sexless groin of a mannequin – while he took her not only uptown but over-the-top, as they met for afternoon tête-à-tête at the Trump Tower and breakfasts at Tiffany's. She bought him a hope chest full of kinky sex tricks and cool cachet; he gave her a pied-a-terre in Manhattan, a membership to the Sidney Biddle-Barrows chapter of the DAR, and an American Express Platinum card. Thus, while it was Peter who popped the question exactly six months after that first dinner date, it was Leota who proposed Las Vegas for the ceremony. That way, she later explained to Oleta, the affair would be both legally binding and tongue-in-cheek. As they each said 'I do' in the little white aluminum-sided chapel, each would also be implying 'I don't' – would be both tying the knot and symbolically untying it at the same time. Because only through the slackness of ambiguity, she explained, could their desire for each other be given free rein. After all, everyone knows that marriage is the noose of the libido. Peter, of course, was charmed by her reasoning, and thanked Oleta privately at the reception for introducing him to Leota. In the photo Oleta took a few minutes later of Leota feeding him a forkful of torte, his face clearly expresses that he is both having his cake and eating it too.

But Peter says that the cake Leota serves after lunch in honour of her sister's arrival – a foot-high caramel and cream confection sculpted to look like a miniature medieval castle – is too delicious to keep. While Oleta takes just a small piece of the wall around the moat and Mrs K refuses a piece altogether, explaining that she cannot eat a work of art, Peter consumes not only the remainder of the wall, but the drawbridge made out of a chocolate bar, the cupcake turrets, the gumdrop-studded battlements and the entire façade with its masonry of non-pareil.

And now the rubble of the cake has been put away and Leota is stacking the Royal Doulton in the dishwasher. Mrs K has fallen asleep in her chair. Peter, having wiped the last crumb of cake off his plate with his finger, has gone to pack up his golfing gear. Oleta offered to help Leota, but she refused. Which is odd; when they were young her sister had always managed to slip out of her chores with a Houdini-like ease. The clear plastic tubing inserted into the crook of Leota's arm, which is faintly tinged with blood and bound in place with a sheath of gauze and shiny transparent tape, makes her look vaguely robotic and the absurd thought crosses Oleta's mind that this is not her sister but some sort of biotechnical impostor. How Leota would gloat if she knew – she's always looking for an opportunity to deceive. Even now, as Oleta watches her rinse a walnut-handled knife under the tap, she can see that Leota is making an elaborate dumb show out of the fact that she knows enough not to put it in the dishwasher. Tenderly she wipes the blade dry on her apron, which is red and white with a Gemini motif and complements the navy and white dress from Daffy's, which she is wearing underneath. Clearly this is another elaborate piece of performance art, a pastiche of some boob-tube fantasy, a cathode ray phantasm concocted out of half-remembered Betty Crocker commercials one marijuana-fogged afternoon. As if to confirm Oleta's theory, she casually looks over her shoulder and asks:

– Would you like to see my cake album?

Oleta decides to play along – after all, Leota is ill. Alas, she is ill, and now she will never make it as an artist, despite the fact that throughout their primary school years, the art teacher always told Mom that Leota, who could produce a perfect copy of anything she saw, was the talented one. That's what Miss Novak said, even though Oleta believes that she made some very interesting and imaginative drawings. The fact that no one could tell that her fish were fish or mistook her submarines for cigars showed the limits of their powers of observation, not hers. Sometimes a cigar is not just a cigar and if Miss Novak had looked a little closer she would have seen the tiny periscope sticking out from just behind the prow. And if Oleta had not been discouraged early in life, perhaps she would have become an artist like Leota. But instead of being considered 'good at art,' or anything else, she was good in itself. Or rather, 'good as gold' – which may be why she went on to earn a bachelor's degree in business, to show that she was good *at* gold as well.

Each photograph has been blown up to eight by ten inches. The first cake has been made to look like a Scottie dog and there are views from the top and side to show its tartan plaid coat of red and green frosting, along with a close-up of its black, licorice-string beard. Leota says:

– That one was for the little boy, who lives down the road, after Peter accidentally ran over his puppy.

The next cake is a flowerbed, dark-chocolate frosting planted with peonies, roses, petunias and a border of pansies and marigolds, all carefully constructed out of minute dabs of coloured sugar. Leota explains that this one was for the old woman next door, who used to work in her garden every day until she had a stroke. After that a yacht, with pretzel-stick masts and cross trees, fruit-roll sails and even a porthole of shaved rock candy, for a college friend of Peter's who'd recently lost his job to downsizing. And so on – thirty pages of photos of cakes shaped to look like a Great Dane, a dude ranch, a Caribbean beach, a hot air balloon, the Venus de Milo, a cat's-eye marble, a bear skin, a buzz saw, a paddy wagon, a Persian carpet, a flock of pigeons flying out of a top hat, and so on – constructed out of everything from Andes mints to ziti, to mitigate every degree and kind of misery.

– Well? Leota asks. – What do you think?

– Well . . . Oleta cannot think of anything to say. She really is at a loss for words to respond to this confectioner's catalogue of loss. And then she turns over the last page. At first she has trouble focusing, and all she sees is a strange brownish blob like carnage on the roadside. Then gradually her brain begins to recognize the thing, to comprehend its shape. This cake appears to be some sort of bloated brown crab, its body coated with a carapace of bitter chocolate, with hairy segmented legs constructed, perhaps, of Slim Jims and chocolate shavings. A smattering of red hots and bits of cinnamon stick form its eyes and voracious-looking mouth parts.

– Oh my goodness, what an ugly thing! Mrs K is wide awake and clutching one of the two Revolutionary War-era pewter candlesticks, as if she means to smash it down on the photo of the crablike cake.

– It's not a thing, Oleta says as she reaches across the table and gently prises the candlestick from Mrs K's fingers. Because suddenly she knows what the cake is supposed to be.

– It's a deer tick, isn't it?

Leota lifts her chin, and it seems as if for just a second Oleta sees *her* and then she is gone, disappearing like a familiar face swallowed up in a crowd, a host of strange nuances of voice, expressions and gestures. But then who is the woman whose chin drops in a nod, whose eyes fall into her lap? She peers at Leota more closely and sees that she is greatly changed, and it's not just the tube in her arm, the dark circles under her eyes or the lankness of her hair. Because her eyes have been shadowed and her hair lank before, and always these were the accessories of the darkness she wore like a ball gown, as her imagination danced until dawn under the bright and feverish lights of her studio. If this is not her sister, then where has she snuck off to?

All afternoon, as Peter golfs the tranquil greens of the New Canaan country club and Mrs K sails the halcyon waters of sleep, Oleta searches anxiously for her sister. Searches for Leota, as she follows this woman about the house and sees her straighten a painting on the wall, and then re-straighten it, dust a crystal vase and then re-dust it, polish silverware until it gleams and then re-polish it, re-wash clothes that are already clean, re-make beds that are already made, watch a soap opera on TV and then re-watch it with the VCR, until it begins to seem as if every image has an after-image, as if every gesture is a copy. But a copy of what? Or a copy of whom? A copy of her real sister, the original Leota? Then who was the genuine Leota? But then she notices that the plastic tube in her sister's arm is filling up with blood – probably from the exertion of all this duplication – and speculation gives way to the need for paramedical action. She must get her to stop, to sit down and rest.

   – Come on, Leota, let's go sit outside, she says, taking her sister firmly by the arm without the tube in it.

   She leads Leota through the family room, realizing as she does that it's the one room in the house that they didn't set foot in all day, and out onto the deck, where she eases her into a big Adirondack chair. Then she drags another chair over the redwood planking and drops down beside her. For a long while they sit in silence, gazing at the lawn with its dark border of hemlocks and riotous peony heart. Oleta decides that the pink of the flowers is not just ridiculous but obscene, like a dog's penis, the colour of things that are best kept out of sight.

   – Everyone thinks it's so beautiful here, Leota finally says as a white butterfly lands on her knee and then flits off, bright against the darkness of the grass. She shivers, and then continues. – Especially when the albino deer comes out. Did I tell you about the albino deer? At dusk it looks like a ghost against the trees.

Oleta doesn't want to know, doesn't want to see this thing that is pushing its way to the surface, but then finds she can't refrain from asking, as if driven by some horrible curiosity, like that time she and Leota dug up a rat that their mother had buried in the garden while they were at school and then just stood there after they'd unearthed it, unable to tear their eyes away, staring into the tiny pink cavern of its mouth. Only it's not curiosity, not curiosity at all that compels her to ask:

– Do you think it's beautiful?

Leota doesn't answer at first. She just sits there perfectly still, the arm with the pink-tinged tube lying on the wooden armrest of her chair like some sort of specimen on a dissecting tray. Then suddenly the arm twitches. And twitches again. At last she blurts out:

– No, I hate nature. I hate that white deer because it looks like a ghost but it's not. Sometimes it walks right up onto the deck and presses its ugly pink nose against the door. And when it leaves its snot is always still there, drying on the glass.

– I hate nature too, Oleta says, realizing as she utters the words that they are true. In fact, she's never really thought much about nature one way or the other. But now it occurs to her that nature is nothing, just a bunch of plants and animals dumbly reproducing, without imagination or embellishment. Nature is nothing and yet people were always talking about it as if it were something, about going back to their roots or returning to their natural colour. But would she and Leota be natural blondes without the existence of the unnatural ones?

And now she has the strangest feeling, the unaccountable sense that she is somehow accountable, like the one she had just a few months ago when she bounced three cheques, the first she'd ever bounced in her life. Even though bank employees had free overdraft protection, she'd carried out a thorough investigation of both all the computer's documents and her own. After twenty minutes of searching (which had meant forfeiting her lunch break), she'd finally discovered the source of the problem: an unrecorded cheque she'd written for a double Martini at the Buffer Zone after finding that she didn't have the cash to cover it and had left her credit card at home. Now, once again, she has the feeling she is somehow accountable, but accountable for what and why? For God's sake, she doesn't even have any records, let alone any notion of what they would record.

– Ever since I got sick I've been getting this headache behind my eyes, Leota says. – It feels like there's something behind the sockets, hammering its way out. She begins to pull lightly at the plastic tube which, tinged as it is with blood, has started to seem like a part of her flesh. A part which could easily be uprooted, like the frailest of umbilical cords. For while clear plastic tape secures the end where the medicine is injected, the other end must have only the most tenuous connection with the vein in the crook of her arm. Oleta watches her, and she can't stop looking, can't stop listening as Leota goes on to say:

– I've only had a headache like this once before, you know. For three days after you made Richard have that accident, until my eyes felt like they were being pushed right out of my head.

After she, Oleta, made Richard get in an accident? But surely her sister is mistaken, surely her sister has misremembered how in a fit of childish resentment, at the peak of pique, she had screamed like a banshee and caused the collision. Surely . . . she is not so sure. For suddenly she is shorn of certainty. Gazing into Leota's pale-blue orbs, those chronically vexing replicas, she cannot be sure that the eyes she saw in the rearview mirror were not her own. Looking at Leota's pale lips, those irksome duplicates, she cannot be sure that it was not her that mouthed the words *ice cream, ice cream*. No, she cannot be sure as she repeats them now, over and over like a chant, conjuring up that dreadful day, that what she said was not in fact *I scream, I scream*. Thus, even if she herself didn't give breath to the fatal shriek – and it's quite possible that she did – can she truly claim she didn't know what was coming? The deadly pun, the malevolent gaze of those eyes in the rearview mirror: the consequences should have been clear a mile off.

– Look, Leota says. – There it is.

Oleta peers in the direction of her sister's finger and sure enough there is the albino deer, floating like a ghost against the dark shapes of the foliage. It bows its head to nibble briefly at a hedge, which in the dusky light also looks strangely insubstantial, as if projected on a screen, then steps out onto the lawn. It starts to amble down towards the deck.

– Stop! Oleta shouts. The deer freezes just before the peony patch. With red eyes like wounds it stares at them over the pink flower tops, then suddenly turns tail and bounds away, its milky form vanishing into the hemlocks. And now everything seems solid and unified once more and for a moment she feels reassured, like when she was a little girl and realized that all she had to do to make the 'ghost' of the wallpaper go away was refocus her eyes. But then she remembers that the sense of safety disappeared as soon as she let them go out of focus again and saw that the 'real' pattern looked as insubstantial as the double. Oleta's skin starts to crawl. Suddenly it is no longer a matter of being first, but of being *there* at all.

– Where's my other half? You told me that I would see him again!

Oleta looks up and sees Mrs K standing in the window of the bedroom overhead, beating her palms and forehead against the screen. Then she looks over at her sister, *her* other half, who is now sitting with her face buried in her knees. What did it matter, she suddenly realizes, who came first, who was the original and who was the copy? The existence of each confirmed the actuality of both, like mutual mirrors. Yes, each countersigned the existence of the other and so what was the point any longer of plastic surgery? Jackie was dead while Leota sat there beside her, a living, breathing replica, speculum of the other woman who was herself.

– Don't worry, Mrs K, Oleta calls. – We're going to try to find him.

– Was that a cow I saw? Mrs K asks as the conductor announces that the next stop is Greenwich.

Oleta answers yes, though it was just a woman in a Holstein print dress, which along with black and white painted lawn furniture, has become a perennial suburban fashion. She smiles at her sister, who is sitting in the opposite seat, next to Mrs K. The closer they get to the city the better Leota looks, like a wilted flower absorbing water or Superman escaping from Kryptonite. Leota winks back. It is understood – no need to mention that no cow hoof has touched this soil for decades. After all, why shouldn't Mrs K enjoy her pastoral dream, a vision of the Connecticut countryside as it most certainly was when she was a young girl living in Brooklyn, when her skin was as soft and smooth as a leaf of new lettuce and her milk teeth had not even begun to loosen? No need to dispel Mrs K's arcadian vision, Oleta thinks, and she listens with approval as Leota tries to help her to bring it into a sharper, more detailed resolution:

– It most certainly was, Mrs K. Not just any cow, but the Dairy Queen. Did you see the big golden bell around her neck? That's to summon all the other cows, who no doubt were on the other side of the clover pasture, just beyond the stone wall.

– Ah yes, the Dairy Queen. I know of her.

Leota goes on to describe her, to fill in the outline that has apparently taken shape in Mrs K's senile brain. She's five feet high at the shoulder, the Dairy Queen – tall and bovinely regal. A truly sovereign cow with a velvety black and white hide, dark melting eyes as mysterious as the womb, and the trembling nostrils of an empath. If you're lucky, you may catch her at sunset, when her golden bell shimmers in the dusky light. But if she starts to hum, to make a sound that bands and disbands over the dark green fields like the wailing notes of an oud, watch out. For her hum inevitably intones death.

– I think I heard her last night, Mrs K quavers.

– There, there, Leota murmurs. – It'll be all right. She slips an arm around Mrs K's bony shoulders while Oleta takes hold of her withered hand – a pose which they maintain through overpass and underpass, as bedroom communities give way to expressways, smoke stacks, billboards and graffiti, until light yields to the darkness that ushers in the city.

'You nearly done in there, Anna?'

Barry's bluff face curves in around the doorway, one plump hand holding the heavy door ajar. Used to his sudden intrusions, I nod in his direction, fully intent on finishing my task.

'Yeah . . . give me ten more minutes.'

'Okey-dokey,' is the easy reply and he is gone.

I continue filling in the area of the left browbone with dusty pink. It complements the pale mauve tints I have blended on to the lids. The colours, in their petal-like softness, give the face a breathing, blooming quality. A final stroke, and with a sigh I lean back on my stool and arc my back to release the tension. The only sound in the room is the faint electric hum from the refrigerated storage units. My hands still clasp the pot of Pink #3 and the applicator brush. I gaze critically at the features yet another time. Yes, the effect is pleasing.

Discarding my materials amid the trays of colours on the trolley to my left, I flex tired fingers. As if my hands know that they have completed the most important part of their work they begin to feel a little numb and cold beneath their thin sheath. I stretch out a latexed index finger and run it over the shape of one brow, then the other. The tiny amount of gel I applied earlier has given them a nice finish.

The brows were in an immaculate state when the girl was brought in. Dark, glossy, with a distinct arch above the bone, obviously well maintained. The lashes don't need any touching up either. They rest on the newly even skin tone my efforts have created. The skin has been the most time-consuming part, as it is the widest area for me to cover, taking in the neck and a shallow décolletage. She has lost a lot of blood. A few days earlier her features would have had a warm vivacity. When I first saw her face it looked drained, with a blueish undertone. Her condition wasn't so pronounced that Ray was needed to work on her with his arterial injections. She had sustained multiple internal injuries, chiefly from ribs to pelvis, but the face, unusually, remained unmarked.

Thanks to the new Dermabase pigment that I've finally convinced Barry to order from the States, the mellow beige I've blended specially creates a dewy look. Rather than pancake the skin, its formula is absorbed, allowing a degree of naturalness. The cheekbones flush, according to the nuances of the ever reliable Pink #3. The lips, framed by the tiniest of laughter lines on either side, are filled in with deep matt rose. I always do lips first, even before skin, and then come back and retouch. I like them to look as if they are about to speak. It helps me focus.

The hands and forearms are deeply lacerated by the impact of shuddering glass. Beneath the pristine sleeves of the dress are several rows of stitches. The white satin gloves are long enough to create no break from one piece of fabric to the other. The driver, Barry told me, went through the glass, but survived.

I like those laughter lines, and the other faint ones echoed around the eyes. They give truth to the photograph the mother gave to Barry yesterday when she came in for the washing and dressing of her daughter. Most clients, except when it involves children, leave that aspect completely to us, but it was made clear from the beginning of this booking that my role would be to assist the mother and two other female relatives; the godmother and an aunt. After their preparations I would work on the face.

The graduation portrait shows a girl given to laughter, her wide smile overriding the academic black enveloping her. Her hair under that silly cap flows in loose brown waves to the shoulders. Right now, this hair is parted austerely in the middle, brushed back and held in a roll at the nape with a net and seven bobby pins.

I've used a coconut-based hair crème to hold it in place, and the thick, sweet smell is quickly brought into sharp relief by the artificial heat of the fluorescent work lights. There's also the faintest lingering of frankincense. I inhale some of the scent and squeeze my sore eyes shut for a moment. My action creates a wild scattering of pin-pricks of light, the shards pressing on the inside of my lids. Time to wrap up. Opening my eyes, I fix my stare on the photo clipped to the side of the trolley, labelled by name; the eyes smiling into mine are brown.

'Yes, Georgina, the effect is pleasing. More than pleasing,' I state into the room's stillness and into that gaze. 'Beautiful.' It makes me feel like I've kept a promise, one that was made yesterday. I glance across to the opposite wall. A whole gallery of mostly colour head-shots reposes there. The second tier is my handiwork, courtesy of Ray's tutelage. Tomorrow, after the delicate veil and headpiece is fitted, Georgina will be photographed and will then repose there too. The door slowly swings open and Barry enters, closing it behind him.

'OK, my sweet? Let's have a looky at what you've done here.'

His tone never doubts for a minute that my work will be effective. I overheard him say to Ray soon after my first client was completed: 'See, mate! I know how to pick them!' Since then he's always just let me get on with whatever's needed doing. Sometimes Ray and I work together, depending on how busy things are, but these days Ray more or less exclusively deals with embalming. He is very generous to me with his experience.

I remove the plastic bib from the girl's chest and give Barry's cheerful face a brief smile. Moving away from the stool, I begin peeling off my gloves. I feel reluctant to step aside, to break from that strange intimacy fostered over a few laborious hours. It was the same with the motorcycle guy, Daniel, but to a lesser degree. I can't really explain it. Sometimes, removing myself is like removing a protective mantle. Of course it is unrealistic. Beyond all logic. I do my best for everybody, but for some I feel more. And yesterday I was allowed to have a place in something that was really private. Tomorrow many pairs of eyes will look upon Georgina. My last service will be fitting the headpiece in the morning, before the body is finally placed in the satin-lined interior. Satin upon satin. Her family will be travelling with her to the church.

'Tilda's just packing up at Reception and I've already locked the Chapel, so go out through the side when you're ready. Michael's due back later tonight. You've done a beaut job, Anna; what we've got here is as pretty as a picture. Thanks again for yesterday's work, the family were really impressed with you.' Barry rubs his hands together, reminding me of how icy my own feel.

'Thanks, Barry.'

He moves closer to me, balls his fists on his hips and peers down to have a closer look at the object clasped in Georgina's gloved hands.

'The icon looks a bit spooky if you ask me. Why do all these heavenly types have such sour-looking faces? Still, you gotta respect a client's request. You live, you learn, though this is the first time we've done someone in their wedding gear.'

One hand brushes the toes of the shiny, silk wedding shoes as he moves around to the other side of the work table.

'Ray says that they never had such a request, not even in Dad's time. If it's the custom in their parts to bury the young unmarried ones in the full gear, then more power to them. I tell you, you see it all here! It gives a whole new twist to "Mother of the Bride", doesn't it?'

He straightens up. His humour annoys me at times, but at least he gives credit where it's due. He's the kind of man that never needs answers from you, as long as he can keep asking questions. 'Anyway, I'll quit my jawing and let you get out of here. See you at eight thirty, my girl.' He turns to pack up, as he describes it.

I uncross my arms and remove my hands from the warmth of my armpits. I look at Georgina as he wheels her away. Mumbling a hasty 'Goodnight' I make for the door. That icon is beautiful in its stylized way. The high foreheads and narrow faces of the Madonna and Child are touched with serenity and tenderness; the delicate paintwork rendered even more striking by the rich silver casing that encloses them. I open the door.

The man sat, head bowed, his hands loosely clasped before him on the shiny, laminated surface of the table. The child sitting opposite stared at him solemnly. She held a glass of juice and, lifting it, took a thirsty sip.

'Are we going to go up now, Daddy?' she asked. Her round hazel eyes fixed him with her enquiry. Her feet perched on the rung of the chair; one foot slid off the wood in the next moment, causing the liquid in the glass to come close to spilling as she rebalanced herself. She gazed anxiously at her father, but he hadn't noticed her near mishap. She let her leg dangle, swinging it gently as she waited for him to reply.

Finally, her father raised his head, his tired, moist eyes taking her in. He gave the merest smile before reaching across and plucking out one side of the Peter Pan collar that was caught under the neck of her cardigan.

'Yes, Anna. Grandma and Aunty Olga should have Mummy ready by now.'

The clear midday light swirled gently in the kitchen around them. He stood up, tall in his dark suit, and held out his hand. Anna carefully put the frosted green glass down and slipped her right hand in his. With a little jump, she came off the chair. She clasped her father's hot hand tightly. They moved out of the kitchen, down the hallway and mounted the stairs. On the way up, Anna stared through the curved banisters; the double doors of the dining room were open and she could see all the sandwiches on plastic-covered trays, the biscuits and small, round almond cakes. All the teacups neatly arranged on one side, just as Aunty Olga had asked her. Grandma had worried she might break one. Many people were coming today to see her mother.

Her father pushed open the bedroom door and guided her in before him. Her mother lay in the centre of the bed. Grandma and Aunty Olga sat on either side, each holding one of her mother's hands. Her grandmother was weeping softly. Aunty Olga held out an arm and Anna went to her, placing her cheek against her Aunty's rough, navy blue wool shoulder. Her father, stood at the foot of the bed, had spoken to her yesterday about all the things that would happen today.

Her mother's skin and her lips and cheeks were so pale, making her loose hair look darker as it curled into her neck. She had been sick for a long, long time and she'd known she was going to die. She had explained to Anna that dying was the only way now that the terrible pain in her tummy would go away. Anna had understood and explained it to her father.

The figure in the bed was dressed in a soft pink nightgown. Anna had never seen her mother wearing it before. The small line of ruffles decorating the chest were just visible above the flower-embroidered bedspread that covered her. Anna spoke close to Aunty Olga's ear: 'Today, she doesn't look like Mummy.' Aunty Olga hugged her with both arms. The doorbell sounded, with a metallic ring.

Deep in the afternoon, when Anna was tired of people touching and kissing her, she quietly climbed the stairs and went to the bedroom. She opened the drawer of her mother's dressing table and immediately found what she was looking for. Her mother hadn't used the burnished gold compact and matching lipstick case for a long time. Anna carried them to the bed and climbed on to the coverlet. Her mother's hands were placed closely along her sides. Anna patted the one with the wedding ring. She then carefully opened the compact and generously whirled the little powder puff around in it. When satisfied, she brushed it over her mother's face, once, twice, three times. Putting the compact down, she reached for the lipstick. She took the lid off, then unfurled it by twisting the bottom part. As the rich red emerged, it released the strong, waxy scent of roses that Anna remembered her mother's kisses once smelling of. She slowly filled in the top and bottom lips, trying her best to keep within the outline of her mother's mouth. She then put two dabs of colour on the cheeks, as she had watched her mother do, and blended them in with an index finger.

'Anna?' Aunty Olga was standing in the doorway. 'Darling, what are you doing?'

Anna turned, startled, showing the lipstick in one hand and the crimson-stained index finger of the other.

'I'm making her look like Mummy.'

Clare Birchall
In the Shade

For Polly Russell

We are on holiday. We say the word with care, as if we can prolong it with kindness. Neither of us wants to leave. There is joy here and we don't ask why.

On the main drag of this small island resort there are tavernas advertizing English breakfasts for one thousand drachmas. A sign outside one reads: *Today's special – Chicken Gordon Blue*. Gift shops sell fake designer T-shirts, sometimes with one letter changed: *Kuppa* or *Nuke*.

We say we're reinventing the package holiday. Which really means we are in bed by ten p.m. with a cup of weak tea, waiting to insert our homemade cotton-wool earplugs, instead of down the beach bar drinking cocktails with names like Greek Mystique and dancing with the local waiters. Not that there is anything wrong with waiters. We go to the same restaurant every evening because we like the slim hips and gentle voice of Spiros, the patient way he tells us how to make dolmades. The real reason is Sally's hip. It had been replaced earlier in the year and dancing was out of the question. She is too young to have such an operation and she jokes about aged things taking over her body. She imagines things like blue rinses and bridge descending upon her life, taking the place of her actual interests and appendages, like a body snatcher. She warns me that if this happens she will not entertain nostalgia, but will celebrate her new identity. She says I'd better watch out because when we come on holiday next year she's going to be singing the praises of the local bingo hall.

'Yes, bingo. Without irony or a sense of kitsch, and then where would you be?' she asks.

'Not here,' I reply, thinking about how she stumbled over the words 'next year'.

We always come to this quiet spot amid the rocks at the furthest end of the beach. It's quite an effort for Sally to walk this far but she says it's worth it to see the naked bathers who seem to congregate here. As if the rocks can punctuate their nudity. Create a syntax of skin.

There's one group of men in their late sixties. Fat and robust, every inch of their skin taut not from muscle but from the filling. Skin that will sag eventually when their appetites go. They're all bald, their heads reflecting the sun like waxed apples. Every day they build a makeshift camp from bamboo sticks and old towels. It provides minimal shade but gives them a sense of purpose. Each morning they set about their task in a military fashion. They remove their clothes in the same manner – with efficiency. Their economy allows no room for eroticism.

I always forget whether art critics describe life models as nude or naked and which word is infused with erotic implications and which is not. I forget which refers to a body that just happens to have no clothes on. Whichever it is, they are it. Their bodies are neutered. Sex has been erased from them; the faint lines are all that remain. They run into the sea at various intervals; their urgency makes us think they are going in to pee. We can see the way their penises are burnt from the Mediterranean sun, and it makes us wince. They're bright pink from head to toe and still they douse themselves in locally pressed olive oil instead of the total sunblock that I have been told to use.

I sit here wearing a large woven sunhat and a loose silk wrap. El mariachi without the songs.

'Can I still sunbathe?' I asked the doctor as he talked with my melanoma in a Petri dish on the table. It sat between us like a dog with two owners both calling its name. Except neither of us wanted it.

'As long as you wear total sunblock, yes, of course.'

'No, I said can I still sunbathe, not can I sit in the sun.'

'You've got to be really careful. Have you ever seen a dermatologist with a suntan?' he asked me.

'I just thought that was because they're all highly diligent professionals, dedicated to the science of saving lives and providing cosmetic surgery with no time for frivolous excursions, gardening or barbecues.' I stared at my forearm, at where the stitches still itched. I pinched the sagging, pale underside to make myself concentrate. I had so much skin; surely they could cut half of it out and I'd still be left with enough for one whole person?

'Maybe the mole wasn't getting bigger, maybe I was getting smaller. We didn't think of that at the time, did we?' I was going to make him smile if it killed me. 'Look, what if I promise to stay away from the sunbeds, keep it natural?' I suggested, mock hopeful.

'That would be like me telling someone with lung cancer to smoke lights.'

'And good advice that would be too.'

I knew the score, I just wanted someone to know how hard it was going to be. How having a tan with a body like mine was like being unexpectedly upgraded to first class on a long-haul flight. It dulled the boredom and increased the chance of meeting eligible men.

An ex-lover once likened the moles on my stomach to stars. I took it as a kind gesture. He was an alchemist, making base metals into gold, donating the prefix 'extra' to 'ordinary'. Star wars. Now it's me watching my body like an astronomer, looking for new formations, an aberration in the night sky of my skin, praying for one to disappear. Wishing for – not on – a shooting star.

The old men are treading water beyond a rock, bobbing. Their faces calm and serious. Occasionally, one will look down as if to check that he's still all there. As if parts of their bodies could be nibbled away by desperate fish without them knowing. I imagine them discussing affairs of state or strategies of war. Behind my closed eyes I make up jokes about the body politic.

Sally and I always go on holiday once a year. We decided to do this many years ago when each doing a Ph.D..

She had said, 'I want to do this every year whether there are men on the scene or not.'

I was single and thought it a marvellous idea. She was not, which made it sound all the more noble.

'I mean,' she continued, 'if you ever get a boyfriend you'll still need a break, it's only healthy.'

'What do you mean "if"?' I demanded.

My dating record is a constant source of amusement. One of the reasons we could go out at night together when we were young was that we had such different tastes in men. She went for what she called 'real men' who had to have hair on their chests and big noses while I went for 'hairless wonders'. 'Boys who provided no chance of commitment or sexual gratification,' as she told me. She was right, of course, but I liked it that way. I thought I'd change, that my tastes would get more realistic as I aged. Even though I'm forty, a young boy with curly black hair, pecs that you could play chopsticks on and no bum to speak of can still turn my head. I haven't cottoned on to the fact that I can't turn theirs. I just don't *feel* forty and I don't want forty-year-olds to feel me. People look and stare when Sally good-naturedly calls me a pervert.

She was the one to get married and have children *and* become a professor before me. I am still only a lecturer after all this time. She became my boss, the head of my department. In open seminars and discussion groups I'd say things like, 'I think Lorrie Moore is the best short-story writer in America today.' And she'd look up above her nose-perched glasses, pause for effect, ask, 'Do you really?' To make me say emphatically, 'Yes, I do.' Then she'd say, 'Good for you,' and proceed to talk about Carver or Cheever while attentive postgrad students wrote detailed notes.

We'd both written our theses on feminist theory. We were both feminists. Now our younger colleagues were encouraging us to be post-feminists, an issue we contemplated on the beach.

'Do you think "women" spelled with a y is more politically correct?' she ponders.

'Wasn't he in the Stones? You know, the guy who went out with Mandy Smith, the fifteen-year-old model? Bill Wyman.'

'I mean, why do you think young girls always say, "I'm not a feminist or anything but . . ."?'

'Hang on, they're not feminists and they're not *anything* . . .'

'And now we're being blamed for giving feminism a bad name.'

'Ha. As if there could be a good name for the redress of patriarchal power and fight against centuries of oppression.'

'Feminism just isn't what it used to be.'

'That's what they said about nostalgia,' I say, whimsically.

When she heard about my skin condition, Sally tried to persuade me to go somewhere other than Greece.

'We could go to New York or Venice, be really cultural,' she suggested.

'But I *teach* cultural studies. I'm always *really cultural*. I just want to be real.' She understood. We'd both been drawn to the sun, had allowed light and blue sea to quicken our senses, to bleach out our thoughts like exposed film. I wanted to return to the scene of the crime.

We only let ourselves read sex and shopping novels on holiday, but this year even that had been spoiled because Sally was setting up a course on popular romance novels. When we were younger we banned all academic talk for this one week. We'd discuss old soap operas, debate whether Krystle or Sue-Ellen had the better lip tremble, and ask things like, 'Who *did* shoot JR?' We'd play the crying game, the object of which was to tell the saddest story you knew in order to make the other weep. Sally was much better at it than me, relating true tales of children's last wishes being fulfilled and orphans dressing up to attract prospective parents. Or maybe I just cried more easily. I'd tell her my father's bad jokes, the ones he saved for Christmas dinner. They were always sexist. Hard to swallow, like the out-of-date confectionery he'd pass round. And we would walk for miles and miles through hills scattered with cypress trees that stood to attention in the otherwise lazy afternoons.

This time, without walking and sunbathing, we fall back onto our intellectual life to keep us company. And we talk about her hip and my skin. I refer to them self-importantly as 'Our Afflictions'. We both swallow the word 'cancer' and I notice how she touches her hair every time I mention chemotherapy. I won't know if I need it until I return for a follow-up to see if the surgery has worked.

It's just me and Sally on this part of the beach now. We're eating fleshy tomatoes, watching the juice make new surfaces on the sand, and talking about fear.

'Throughout the eighties, we were taught to fear nuclear war. Remember all that bleak TV, all that glass, all that apocalypse then?' I ask her.

'Hmm. *Threads, When the Wind Blows*.' She shivers in defiance of the sun.

'I hated *When the Wind Blows*,' I say. 'It was somehow worse when it happened to cartoon characters. You just *know* the world should end when cartoons get so . . . so . . .'

'Unfunny?'

'So pessimistic.' I'm on a roll. 'It was a fear that whistled through our bedsheets and rattled our windows. It actually made me not want kids. Sally, we were taught to be afraid of mass destruction and then it just disappeared from the public imagination, like news coverage of famine or prolonged war. We were taught to be collectively afraid. We dreamed of our last minutes. I even made a list of people I would call and pinned it beside the phone. Everyone thought it was the code to my speed dial, but it was my loved ones, ranked and ready to be goodbyed.'

'I remember that. What number was I?' Sally asks.

'Number three.'

'Not bad.'

The sea is reflected in Sally's glasses and I want to swim through them.

'And now there's *this* of all things.' I point to my arm and the small scar that winks at me. 'This that creeps up on me like nobody's business and it's going to stick around long enough to make sure I understand death not as the mythologized inevitable result of some exterior global act of mutual destruction, but as something within me, my own internal invasion.' I'm out of breath and Sally hands me a tissue for the tomato juice that's streaking my arm.

I sit back into the afternoon shadow of a rock. I look at the heat, knowing it will be the last holiday like this, trying not to think through the word 'last'.

We take a final swim before going back to the apartment to pack and make our way to the airport. I stand, looking for the horizon, water up to my chest, my feet being covered by unsettled sand, rooting me against the sway of the tide. Sally swims up behind, her arms finding their way around me and for a moment I cannot tell which are hers and which are mine. She holds on to me, her head sideways to my back, her ear and cheek nestled between my shoulder blades as if she's listening to the secrets within a shell. Our salty skins on each other and her saying, 'I wish we could stay here for ever.'

Paul Barron
Falling Shoe

Three nights in a row Carol and I had gone to bed without speaking. Saturday and Sunday mornings we took turns to wake up first, flushing the toilet as though that could be done spitefully, making coffee, clattering the pot. We stewed on the offences we had suffered, righteous, and the original argument was lost.

But Monday morning was different; we must have touched in our sleep, and I woke up, grateful, with her back against my chest. I brought my lips to the knob of her spine just below her neck and everything I had taken apart over the previous few days seemed restored. The skin below her ribcage felt silky, the minute, pale hairs; she sighed and pushed her buttocks back at me. I stroked the space between her breasts and traced the tender curve of the heavy breast that encroached on the backs of my fingers.

My arm was thrown off. She flung off the blankets and leapt out of bed in the same movement. 'What are you doing?' she said. 'Groping me?'

She had been unconscious, unaware we'd been touching.

Spotting my erection, she gave me a look of disgust and went to shower. I pulled the blankets over my head, gutted and feeling like a pervert.

Drawers rumbled, clothes hissed and spat on their hangers. The blinds shot up with a clang and the small, sad weight rolled off my thigh as I sat up, blinded in the bright room. In her bra, tights and skirt, Carol stood on her tiptoes, rummaging with one hand among the shoeboxes on the high shelf of the built-in wardrobe.

I unrolled the underpants that lay in a ring on the floor, pulled them on, then went over and said into her face, 'The trouble is you would call it "groping".'

She rummaged and rummaged.

'Sex is like everything else to you,' she said. 'You start off as though you've already failed. Everyone's against you, aren't they?'

'Watch yourself,' I said, but she was digging, digging, and the thick-heeled shoe fell and hit her, smack, in the eye.

The next thing I knew she was crying so hard I thought the neighbours would call the police. She went and buried her face in the bed and I stood next to her, holding my hand above her shoulder blade, letting it hover there, and when I lowered it, barely touching her, she shrugged me off violently.

Pacing back and forth through the house, I thought, Why did that have to happen? Now nothing I say will mean anything. She will be in the right. By default, she will be in the right. I tried to read the front page of the paper but nothing could hold my attention.

After half an hour I heard her in the kitchen, talking on the phone. I went through and saw that her eye was turning black and the other eye was swollen from crying. Her nose was full. She was talking to her boss.

'I'm not coming in today,' she said.

He quacked in the receiver.

'I know,' she said. 'I'm sorry. It won't happen again.'

She hung up the phone and I went and put my arm around her, but she tore herself away and gingerly patted the inky skin below her eye.

'I tried to warn you,' I said. 'I could see it coming.'

She gave me an accusing look and thumped across the carpet to the bedroom, shutting the door behind her. I called in sick and stared out of the window at a blackbird chasing a squirrel along the telephone wire. For two hours we stayed in separate rooms.

When she reappeared, the eye was fat. She wore jeans and a sweatshirt and this time when she went to the phone it was to call her mother. Her voice was thick and sad.

'No, I'm fine,' she said, 'but I can't meet you for lunch . . . getting things done around here . . . sorting out the wardrobe.'

She hung up the phone and snatched up her car keys.

'Where are you going?' I said.

She didn't speak. She pulled out a tissue, then said, 'To buy a rack for the shoes.'

'What about your eye?' I said.

'What about it?'

She pushed things around in a drawer until she found sunglasses.

'What if I drive you?' I said.

'I can drive myself,' she said, but the anger had gone from her voice and she sounded depressed.

'No,' I said. 'I will. I want to.'

With her sunglasses on, the taut skin shone between the fair hairs of her eyebrow. And in the car, behind the lenses, her eye reminded me of the upturned cowrie shell in the basket on the back of our toilet.

In the DIY centre I followed her with the trolley and picked up tools and pieces of white plastic pipe, biding my time until things between us could return to normal. It had started raining and buckets were placed on the floor to the catch drips from the leaky roof. Passing the taps and shower fixtures a woman and a teenage girl appeared to be talking about us. I looked back at them and the woman pursed her lips as though she were about to say something to me. She said nothing and I kept on walking. Beneath the piped music, just before the clash of a ladder, I heard the word 'coward'. Further along, an old man stared back and forth between us. He was dropping screws into a paper bag, moving his lips narrowly. At the checkout I watched the hands of the cashier. They were tattooed with matching snakes. She blinked at me sulkily and asked Carol in a confidential way for £67.49.

I wanted to say to Carol, 'People think it was me who smacked your eye.' But after we'd argued, I always found it was better to keep things simple and put up with the incidentals, the garden hoses and checkouts. Arguments only ever seemed to heal when we let them, when we stared out of windows at the rain, which was how we travelled home.

I set about emptying the wardrobe: the shoes in the boxes on the high shelf; the loose, misshapen shoes on the floor; the suitcases; skirts; suits; dresses; shirts; trousers; assorted coat hangers; dry cleaning bags; the three shopping bags stuffed with unsorted papers. The bed was piled high with clothes. With a mess all around me, Carol came in and said, 'I never saw myself in this sort of marriage.'

My back was to her. I thought about keeping my mouth shut.

'And I did?' I said. I could have gone on but I turned around to see that the white of her eye was stained piteously blue.

'I'm too fragile,' she said.

I wanted to remind her of how destructive she could be, but such a small blow had played havoc with her face and I already regretted so much.

'I'll make you some cocoa,' I said.

She looked pathetic, blotted and lopsided. She smiled and let me coax her onto the couch. I tucked a blanket around her legs. Again she smiled, and the feeling I'd had that morning returned – there would be peace for a while. It was marred only by something she'd said that I couldn't put my finger on. All that went around in my mind was that people would jump to conclusions. People would see the black eye and think she was a certain type of woman; they would think of me as a certain type of man.

For the rest of the week she wore sunglasses to work and saw no one else until Saturday when her mother arrived at our door. I was reading in the next room and could hear them through the wall.

'We haven't seen you for a while,' her mother said. 'I thought I'd just check in to make sure everything's all right.'

'Everything's fine,' said Carol.

There was a silence and then Carol said, 'He's getting some work done next door.'

'It's all blue and yellow. By your nose,' said her mother. 'You've got a black eye.'

'Oh, that,' said Carol. 'A shoe fell out of the wardrobe.'

'Really?' said her mother. 'A shoe.'

'Yes,' said Carol. 'A shoe.'

There was more silence.

'Really,' said Carol.

'Anyway,' said her mother, suddenly cheerful, 'I came round to invite you for your teas.'

'It's fine,' said Carol. 'It's nothing.'

Her mother had had her late in life, the only child, and her parents were both over sixty-five. When we arrived for tea, her father was sitting in front of the television watching football. He glanced over at us, then back at the football.

'Hi, Dad,' said Carol.

'Hello,' he said.

'Hi, George,' I said.

Her mother paraded around with a glass dish. When she came to me I saw there were four raw steaks in it. 'Look at these beauties,' she said. They were sirloins, thick and cold-looking, trimmed with rinds of hard, white fat. Good on black eyes, was all I could think.

George looked at them grudgingly.

'I've been getting them wholesale,' said Carol's mother.

She talked for a while about the wholesale warehouse, Carol nodding in encouragement.

'I'll let you know when I'm going next time,' she said. 'We'll stock up your freezer.'

I went over and stood next to George's chair.

'What's the score?' I said.

He said nothing and kept his eyes on the football.

I got the same treatment later when we were eating and I asked him to pass the potatoes. This time Carol and her mother were there to notice. We all sawed at our steaks – steak, steak, steak – putting pieces of it into our mouths and no one said the other thing that steak was good for. The silence was the sort that descends upon a family, the sort you feel when you weren't born into it, the scrape of a chair, the clinking of knives on plates. George's nose whistled. I wanted to say something to clear the air, but George spoke. He said it to the tablecloth. 'Tell me how you got a black eye, again?'

I watched Carol as she described what happened. She tilted her head. She was upbeat. 'You know the shoes, Mam. The platform heel?' her smile was thin. She didn't mention that we'd been arguing; perhaps this was how the false cheeriness crept into her voice. Her mother watched her father's eyes. He was grim, and I could see the whole thing had come off sounding like a lie.

Christine Anne Thomas
Underwater Breathing

Outside the long, square window, the rain glitters down through the yellow glow of the street lamps, washing the air and the pavement with quick lashes and gentle sheets. The sounds of the night are enlarged in the darkness – far-off sirens and car horns, clouds of laughter from people stopped in conversation on the street below, mindless of the rain. The endless parade of voices and cars entrances Rowan and she forgets for a moment where she is. She isn't in one of the small, one-bedroom flats that make up this converted brick house; she's not standing in the galley kitchen while Tai readies for bed in the bathroom. She doesn't hear the water running and the incessant hum of his electric toothbrush. But when he comes out, her shoulders flinch at the sharp click of the door as it opens; she tenses at the dull groan he makes as he settles into bed. Still staring outside but aware now of every sound inside, she thinks of his skin, damp and puffy from the shower, his teeth gritty from the power brush, his heat and his slightly sour smell.

I would think he lived alone here but for a few of her clothes hanging in the closet, some thin glass bottles of perfume and lotions on the dresser. Though they share the flat, it is *his* place. Rowan has only been in this town for a year and has staked no claim; she is a long-term guest. I'm not sure if Tai even realizes that she has left the room. He's enveloped in the warm buzz of feeling everything is as it should be; that the world he has always wanted has been achieved. That buzz has also created a false awareness, a kind of sleepwalking through the days and dinners, the conversations of his life.

Really, though, he loves her. I can see that he does. And she cares for him. But she will be gone in the morning and he won't know why or what for. There'll be nothing he can comb through to find meaning, nothing left except the absence of any trace of her. His world will be shattered; hers will feel fresh and reborn. He will be confused and disbelieving, then angry and bitter. What can I do? She is a destroyer of worlds; it is the only way she can save her own. Get out first and get out quick. She learned that the hard way. Years ago.

It has been nearly two years. I think she will feel more clean when it has been exactly two. As if two years were some sort of sentence she has to wait out before the doors clank open and she is released.

When Rowan first moved here she was alone, she had never been here and she knew no one who lived nearby. It was far away from the place where she was before, which was all that mattered. She had no trouble finding work and in the first few weeks she'd met Paul, a history teacher at the college. He became a close friend – well, to Paul it seemed more than that, but for Rowan that was all it would ever be. He introduced her to Elsa at a faculty party, and they'd spent the night laughing and talking easily. Rowan had suggested they go for coffee. *I don't have any girlfriends here*, she told Elsa, *I guess men are easier to meet*. Elsa had agreed with a serious nod. *You know what you're dealing with, with men – basically anyway.*

I know there was a time when Rowan didn't feel this way about men, but now she knows they're capable of doing painful hurtful things. And some even enjoy doing them. The trick is to see the signs coming as far ahead as possible. Either that, or don't jump in at all. It's a tightrope, really, stretched above a deep, murky pool.

Sitting at an outside table at a café on campus, Elsa had asked Rowan about Paul. Rowan gasped as she inhaled her cigarette smoke and looked out at the sky. She sent the smoke circling above their heads before she replied.

Oh, it's nothing. He wanted it to be something, but I can't do serious any more, she told Elsa, laughing.

Even now, whenever she mentions that other time, she speaks almost flippantly, as though she's making a joke, except she is the only one left with a smirk on her face. When she looks into the other person's eyes, the smirk slides into a soft upturn of compassion – for them, for having to hear the overspill of her thoughts, and for herself too.

Taking a last breath of smoke and pressing the smouldering cigarette end into the ashtray, Rowan answered Elsa's question. *I don't even remember enough to say.* It's not true – this not remembering – though she wasn't lying. There are many things she doesn't remember and can't: not in a scared, something-is-hiding-in-the-shadows kind of way, but because it is impossible. She simply can't. It might be better that way, since memories give things life, make them more real sometimes than they were before.

Really, it's all simple and boring. Girl meets boy, girl loves boy; girl loses self through boy's siphoning grip, but escapes at the crucial moment. A fairy tale, gone wrong but right again, of course.

I could see Elsa hanging on these words but seeming not to, trying not to risk quieting Rowan with a bold show of attention. It was the first she'd heard of Rowan's past, and I know it was the first Rowan had spoken about anything apart from her world here. Elsa was smart; she knew that if they both were nonchalant, if they both acted witty and light, then nothing had any meaning but right now. And she was right, because that was the only way Rowan was able to speak about it. So, since she doesn't smoke, Elsa busied her hands with the coffee cup and looked not at Rowan, but at the backs of the wrought-iron chairs at the next table.

I can tell you though, Rowan continued, *I know, I mean I* absolutely *know, if I hadn't left at that moment I would have been dead, or near to it, physically anyway.*

She can't see what I see, remember what I know. About what was expected, what was performed. I know about it as though I've seen video footage of it, only closer. Every time he grabbed her arms with his sweaty white-but-not-white fingers, squeezing them like dough, I could feel her spine scraping on the wall, her hair gritting and complaining, pressed tightly onto the back of her head as she tried to move. Each time he pushed her I could feel his laugh circling like icy nails around my head.

She always had bruises then, she does remember that. And the bites that were supposed to be fun, normal, loving. Now she knows most of what happened wasn't all right, wasn't supposed to be. She knows some of it could be definitively called many names, official and hollow-sounding titles for events that felt muddled and heavy. Other things that he did just fell into categories, lists under broad and not-so-broad headings. *Abuse: spitting (in face, eyes); kicking, throwing (i.e. her, at walls; or things at). Weapons Used: knives, ropes, scissors. Rape: all kinds.* You get the idea.

It was only months that she was with Tai, but even short spells of time can be constricting. After leaving his flat, and then her things at Elsa's, Rowan walks easily down the street with no destination in mind. The moment she left, her mind cleared and he became the past, distant, though it was just hours before that she had laid next to him, his legs touching hers under the covers. She had opened the door, breathing in the new, early-morning air, and walked out feeling she could be anyone, she could be anywhere.

At her favourite sandwich shop, one that is tucked away on a narrow side street, she decides to stop and eat an early lunch. She likes the nearly empty room better than her Brie and tomato baguette. Sitting at a small table close to the wall, she stares through the window, watching the mothers out walking their children, the babies wilted and the older ones too tired to cry; the lanky men hiding in their suits and ties, looking straight ahead but nowhere at all. No one else comes in and no one notices she is watching. All of a sudden, Rowan, pierced by memories, almost forgets that she is there.

She worked in a sandwich shop then, in a small neighbourhood of a city she hasn't seen for almost two years, making lightly singed hamburgers for the writer who lived around the corner with her five cats, and vegetable baguettes thick with cream cheese for the lady post deliverer. The owner called the place the Triple A Café after his wife and two daughters, though he never saw them. When it wasn't that busy he was across the block talking business at the Irish pub, the kind of business that involved several pints and many cigarettes.

On the nights when she closed late, after all the potatoes were peeled and the fresh food tightly wrapped, he would pour her a small drink while she ate dinner. They would talk uncertainly to each other about the last customers or what needed to be ordered, and he would get close. He would put his arm around her and say her name softly, talking still but meaning something different, and he would try, kind of, to kiss her. When she left he would lock the door behind them and go back to the bar, never home. *Goodnight Ray*, she would call over her shoulder, not wanting to see him stumbling across the street or, worse, staring at her retreat.

On those nights her own home felt safe, comfortable, though she never knew what to expect from one night to the next. Even that had become familiar, dependable. Thinking of it that way, you can see how the abnormal becomes reasonable, right, the way it should be because it is the way it is. She'd bring him home food from the shop and tell him she was able to take it for free. I know that if he knew she had paid for it, then the sandwich would go uneaten, thrown unopened in the rubbish can. He acted like her supporter, wanted it to seem as though he never took from her or forced her into anything at all. It was in this way that she offered everything herself, voluntarily.

Most times, he would be waiting for her, thinking she was late and who had she been talking to? Other times, he would be out somewhere unknown and she would leave the sandwich in the refrigerator and wait for him in bed. Because if she had brought nothing, that would be worse than anything else. I go over it again and again, thinking, it is just a sandwich – even though I know better than anyone that it was much more than that. This was just one of the rules that had to be followed. He's not the only one, there are many who lead these enclosed, ordered lives. Many who need someone else to control in order to survive themselves. To see his parents together was an affirmation, a tacit approval of this way of life.

Outside again, the light rain falling on a moving roof of

Underwater Breathing

umbrellas, Rowan wonders about where she could go, a country to visit, or maybe a road to drive down – long and with plentiful vistas. Long roads intrigue her – ones that stretch across wide spaces of land, seemingly endless, but whose destinations you can't know for sure until you follow them. She is thinking about leaving town today, tomorrow, without saying a word to anyone.

Even though she is in a completely different neighbourhood to where they lived, Rowan still glances around, almost instinctively, as though Tai could find her. She doesn't want to see him or anyone, no one she knows, though for a second she wonders if he'd even want to see her. She tells herself that he has always known she is quick moving, never settling anywhere for long. In some way, then, he must have known, must have expected this. But that is as far as she can think about it and for as long.

Soon Rowan is lost in the streets and unfamiliar faces. She has nowhere to be and is sure that no one is waiting for her to return.

On that last day she returned in the afternoon to an almost empty apartment. She sat on his double bed – just on the edge of it because to intrude any more onto the surface would force her to feel the damp coolness of the down comforter – and tried not to let the weighted water that threatened to cover her, swallow her entirely. It was so heavy; the effort to breathe caused a terrible sucking compression as her lungs collapsed inward rather than ballooning out with air. I can hardly see, she thought.

As she sat on the edge, the bed seemed to absorb some of the water that pressed tightly around her. It felt sticky and wet like an old discarded sponge. Her awareness stretched into the hallway of the building – she had long since been trained herself to hear the first alarms. The whisper click of the front door of the building locking, the shimmer of its glass panes shaking in weakened frames, the creaks and groans of the carpeted steps under his weighted footsteps. Definitely the sharp scrape of his key being forced into the lock on the door, moulded to fit every pointed edge of the cold metal yet somehow always hesitant, reluctant to yield to the insistent thrust.

Her thoughts moved steadily – from the bedroom, to the door, down the two flights of stairs, to the glass-panelled entryway and up again, only to repeat, repeat, repeat. Somewhere in its pacing of the surrounding walls, her mind snagged on the black backpack propped up by the door – now with three crucial occupants: her address book, her wallet and her keys. They wouldn't usually be collected in one secure place, but would be placed in their ordered locations – keys on the key hook on the wall, wallet on her dresser top, address book by the bedroom phone, bag wherever she had found allotted space to do her reading. Now they were all together, waiting, just in case.

She saw the phone perched on the scratched oak table by the bed, the phone that lit up four green lights when it rang. Her arm stretched out to call, but the alarms sounded as her fingers kissed the cool plastic top and her awareness stretched deeper into the hallway to follow his creaking, forced climb up the stairs. She was certain it was him even before she heard the crush of the key in the lock. Her hand still poised on the receiver, her eyes fixed on the red glow of the digital clock. It burned seven. Impossible – she had come back at four. She hadn't been there on the edge of the bed for all that time, had she? And now he had already returned.

At Elsa's Rowan opens the door. She moves quietly and slowly out of long habit. She had been walking for endless hours, though she couldn't say exactly what she had done. *Oh, just looked in a few shops that I've never had the chance to go in, drank too many coffees. You know, the usual.*

Elsa wasn't asleep, but covered up and reading on the sofa. I'd almost say she was waiting up for Rowan, but of course she would be worried, wondering. She knew only that Rowan was living at Tai's and now she wasn't, that it was better for them both, and she was going to stay with her just for a little bit. Then Tai called Elsa's number, the first on a list he had found, forgotten in the back of a drawer with a pair of black trousers and a grey wool hat, and she had listened to him cry in confusion, asking a woman he didn't know to explain, to intervene.

I guess that's to be expected, Rowan says, sighing as she perches on the arm of the sofa. *I'm sorry you had to listen to him for so long.*

He sounds really destroyed Ro, Elsa replies, maybe you should talk to him or . . . I don't know. Elsa gathers the throw around her and hugs her knees, looking sideways at Rowan. I think she had to say it or she'd've felt she was being unfair to Tai, as if that time spent on the phone had made her obliged in some way.

Rowan doesn't respond, just flips idly through the travel section of the newspaper. A few minutes later, she folds the pages into neat creases and goes to bed.

She was supposed to have met him late that afternoon for a movie. She hadn't gone – had only perched waiting for three hours, her eyes resting blankly on a torn-up tuft of carpet, her thoughts treading, snagging, drifting, following, repeating – and he would be angry. That was normal, at least it seemed that way, didn't it? She had meant to be gone by now, out with a family friend she had only contacted for the first time that week, but it was too late. Her eyes alone jerked up when he kicked the bedroom door.

He leaned stiffly against the doorframe, hands stuffed in the pockets of his jeans, body twisted, skin gripped close and tight at the jaw. *I waited for you, I even kept my coat over a seat next to me the whole time, but you never came. I can't believe you. You made me wait there the whole time.*

I need to talk to you, Mark, she said.

She followed his retreat into the other room and stood in front of his bent figure on the couch, eyes fixed in false attention on the television. She wondered what her voice was going to say next. Trying to block his view did nothing, so she slowly and purposefully turned off the television. She dragged a chair in front of the couch and sat diagonally, only slightly facing him. As she began to talk, his body grew more tense, yet hers slumped, her body letting go as her mind fixed on the words that kept repeating in her head. She just had to get it out, get it said.

She was moving out, she needed to leave. I can't do this any more, she told him. He glared at her, watched her lips move, his hands clasped together were white with strain.

I can't believe this. I can't fucking believe this. You want to move out. You want to move out. Why don't we just end this then?

OK. OK. *You're a fucking piece of work.*

The phone pealed, diluting the room. She rose from the chair, an old woman getting up from her usual spot, and went to answer it. That was Maria, she told him. We're going out to coffee in a few minutes. *Just like that? After what we just said?* We already had plans. *So that's it then.* A deep breath then, Yeah. She watched the skin on his face ripple and seethe and she stiffened in her chair – not too much in case, like an animal, quick motion startled him and made him jump. He bolted up from the sofa anyway. *Fuck you.* The bedroom door slammed and she saw it fold and buckle, the light flashing through on both sides. Somehow already on her feet, her eyes fixed directly on her backpack by the door. Mind and body moved her and she knew exactly what to do.

Outside, not really knowing where to go, her eyes saw the bus stop across the street and her feet beat the ground to the pay phone next to it. She started to dial but couldn't find any numbers, *oh no, oh no* in her mind repeating, repeating, repeat. And then she saw him. He was on the front steps, his head darting in every direction, spotting her. She started walking the opposite way, the receiver dangling on its snake-like metal cord.

You are a cold, evil bitch, Rowan, I hope you go to hell. He had caught her by the arm. Shaking and twitching, hands stuffed back into his pockets, he was barely recognizable. His eyes had switched, uncovering that other person, so different but so familiar. She'd known them both for years, though she never knew which one she would see. She expected him to do something, anything, other than turn and walk away.

In the morning, the smell of coffee warmed the room as Rowan dried her hair. Elsa had made the rich and dark brew for the two of them, setting out spoons next to the cream and raw sugar. The sun was bright through the curved windows, infusing the room with yellow light. The early fog had cleared, leaving light, full clouds moving slowly through the sky like waves.

Rowan had dreamed about water during the night, about being at the bottom of a jelly-like, dark jade pool. Another woman was there, smiling at her. Rowan just stared back at first, then smiled before pushing up towards the sunlight penetrating the top. But as she splashed up onto the surface, Rowan was alone. And when she looked down under the water she could see nothing but darkness; the woman was gone.

Thanks for the coffee, Elsa, Rowan says, taking a mug in her hands.

Elsa motions Rowan to sit down, but she heads to the window instead.

I thought that later we could go for dinner, maybe at that small Italian place across from the Rose Pistola? Elsa is casual, speaking softly, but I can feel the strain behind her words. She wants somehow to ground Rowan again, as though if she can make her stay long enough to eat, maybe then she will stay for good.

We could do that, sure, later – I have a few things to take care of today. I'm serious Elsa, I am going to be out of your way tomorrow. Rowan says this more to the street outside the window than to her, but I can see Elsa's body soften in relief. I know how she feels. Rowan is always one second outside your reach, even when she is so close, right in front of you.

He took every liberty and every precaution. But he never, ever hit her. Just took pieces away a little at a time, some unnoticeable, some large fleshy chunks. He told her it was as though all along he had a piece of clay that he would twist and bend and shape into whatever he wanted it to be. Then all of a sudden it was immovable, unmouldable. She doesn't want to remember this, but tears were filling his eyes. Tears. I saw them come. I watched him sit, hunched and silent on the bed, heaps of clothes and papers and things that had escaped him strewn all around, filling up the spaces. His world, too, had been destroyed.

She tries to think of that time as another life, another her. If she remembers, if she really tries to think about it, she will have lost that much more. He will have taken that much more. Even though that dark red curtain is up, he is always just on the other side of it. So she keeps walking, keeps moving, one step ahead all the time. But I remember, and I am closer still.

She used to be very trusting – still is, though in a different way. She knows in her head that trusting is good, it's what others do with that trust that's bad. But that's the part she's having difficulty getting rid of, the part she can't scrub off. That subtle fear is a second skin surrounding her; in it she can barely breathe, sometimes she can't even feel through to the other side. It's thinner than it was, but it has many, many layers.

Before Elsa wakes, before the alarm sounds to ready her for the day, Rowan slips down the hall leaving the doors, the rooms and the air open wide. Downstairs, she pushes open the glass doors and bathes in the bright light of the day. When Elsa sits down in the kitchen with her cup of creamy coffee, she'll find the yellow piece of paper with her name printed on it in Rowan's big, curly letters. Only then will she realize that the door is standing open and empty, and that she's the only one there.

I could have warned her, could have told her this would happen. I could have told Rowan not to go, to hold out a little longer. But all we could manage, for the first time, was to leave a note and tell her goodbye.

Prague – E-J Major <ej@digitaldreamworld.co.uk>

Ronan Bennett
Havoc, in its Third Year

An extract

W hen the women found milk in her breasts and other secret feminine tokens, Scaife – the constable's man, an archdolt – was dispatched across the windswept moors and icy mountains to fetch Master John Brigge, coroner in the wapentakes of Agbrigg and Morley.

Brigge was reluctant to answer the constable's summons. His wife was pregnant, she was bleeding, and the neighbours and gossips had been called. But the law is the law, duty is duty, and a man defrauds his own name if he but once neglects his office. And this was Brigge's office, his calling: the coroner went wherever there was a sudden or unnatural death, wherever there was a body to view.

A body, for his purposes, might be no more than a jawbone and a finger, or some parcels of rancid black meat worried up by the dogs. It might be a young man gored by a bull, his bowels hurled out, or a gummy old crone brought by despair to a rope fastened from the timbers of a barn.

Or it might be, as it was in this case, a birth-smothered infant.

Brigge lived with ghosts and saints; they were everywhere in his life. To his mind nothing in the world was without signification: dreams were portents, phantoms real, and only a fool believed in such a thing as chance. He could not but note the nature of this particular sudden death coming as it did so soon upon his wife's impending confinement. Gazing at Elizabeth huddled by the fire with her maids and the women, whispers and slow gestures of care and comfort between them, he thought it a very ill omen. He went to the window and lit candles and there,

183

under his breath so Scaife would not hear and inform against him later, he said a prayer in the name of the Father, the Son and the Holy Ghost, as his mother taught him he should:

Whose candles burn clear and bright, a wondrous force and might,
Does in these candles lie, which, if at any time they light,
They sure believe that neither storm nor tempest dare abide,
Nor thunder in the sky be heard, nor any devil spied,
Nor fearful sprites that walk by night, nor hurt by frost and hail.

John Brigge was, secretly and dangerously, of the old religion.

When he had said his prayer and completed his preparations, Brigge admonished Dorcas, Elizabeth's favourite maid, to be assiduous about her mistress and do everything to be a good comfort to her. Then he went to his wife and slipped into her palm a little bottle of holy water, which had been blessed by his confessor, so she would have consolation and protection in the extremes of her labour. About her neck he hung three small eagle-stones, which were brought long ago by ancestors who had once travelled through the groves of Cyprus; stones within stones, bodies within bodies.

Finally, Brigge kissed his wife and said some tender things to her: that he loved her and that with Christ's mercy he would find her and their new child waiting for him on his return. But even as he took his leave, Brigge did not know if he would see Elizabeth again in this life.

Calling Adam, his clerk, from where the boy was mewed up in his chamber as was his custom, the coroner went to the stables and got the horses ready. The three men started on their way.

Winds and rain-winds raged around Brigge's lonely stone house. The land about was poor, that which was not marsh being nothing but cold moor, moss and stones exposed to hard frosts and biting winds. It was known as the Winters. Little grew there. Brigge and his household depended on the black oats he sowed in the sloping field below the house and on the sheep and few cows he pastured on its stubble between harvest and spring planting.

In years gone by, he had profited from his wool and woolfells and tallow and grain, but blight and disease three seasons in a row had reduced him to debt. His creditors, Christian men all, had given him until Christmas. At Christmas, when he was unable to pay, the Christian men redrafted the bonds and presented him with terms which were very harsh but at least gave him until harvest to find the money he owed: if Brigge's harvest failed again this year, so would he.

His horse walked on and the coroner took a last look over his meagre estate. Foreboding welled up in his heart. Like all men on the brink of disaster, he desperately wanted to know the future. He wanted to know how things would stand a year from now, in five years, ten. He looked ceaselessly for signs and struggled with their meanings – a robin's return to a branch, the shape of a cow's aborted foetus, the bud of a wild flower where none had grown before. Signs could be hidden and hard to discern; sometimes they were obvious and overlooked for trifles.

Although it was not yet midday, the light was the grey of the deep cold sea and fringed with silver. The wet snow raked the men and gales blew with such force that Brigge felt it must be God's will to prevent his journey, though he could not understand why the Almighty should want to frustrate him in the performance of his lawful office.

As they approached the high pass where the snow was thickest on the ground, the wind gradually died away. There they dismounted and led the horses until a freezing mist, thick as milk, came down and enfolded them in pure whiteness and silence and the world became an empty, lost place. They had no choice but to halt and wait, for a blind foot in these breakneck mountains would certainly be fatal.

While they waited, Brigge questioned Scaife about the infant, inquiring whether the child appeared to have come before its time. The dolt could not say and seemed to think the question a trick, regarding Brigge slyly with a stupid, popping, fat grey eye. Brigge asked about the one the constable had apprehended, taking her to be, as was the usual circumstance in these sad cases, a young girl who had consorted lewdly with a fellow servant or with her master. He imagined her waiting for him, already overcome by remorse of conscience, the Machine of the World collapsed and fallen in around her, her head dissolved in tears.

Scaife answered that this one was no girl but a full woman of thirty or more years who had come out of Ireland and was on her way to Nottingham where her supposed husband was, as she alleged, and that her name as she gave it was Katherine Shay. Her manner, Scaife continued, was not sorrowful in the least, but prideful and very brazen and uncontrite. What else could be expected from one such as she, he asked, singing the refrain of the times, who was part of the horde of foreigners and idle wanderers and vagrants who plagued the good people of these parts and were like locusts descending on the corn of Egypt?

Brigge, his heart as sentimental and volatile as that of any man soon to be a father – and more quick to extremes and turns of emotion because this was Elizabeth's first conception to come to full term – listened in horror and asked himself what sort of woman this could be who had killed her child and yet did not repent.

John Brigge filled up with loathing and revulsion for Katherine Shay.

Presently, the mist shrank back sufficiently for them to lead the horses on through the pass. But as they went, Brigge's mare grew nervous. The declivities here were very sharp, the paths perpendicular, cracked and without integrity. Stones trickled treacherously away at the side with the sound of faint, descending notes, a frozen musicality, and the horse snorted and strained against him.

Scaife looked back over his shoulder and said, 'You shall not fall, your worship, if you are but brave.'

For this, Brigge gave him the hard words that were his due and commanded the fool to get on. The coroner was not afraid of falling but the foreboding he had experienced as he left the Winters now gathered into dread. He could not be sure of its causes – his fears for Elizabeth, his horror at Katherine Shay, the storms around him or the black sky above? – but the apprehension was strong in him that the summons he had answered this morning was already taking him further than was safe to go.

As he picked his way over the crumbling rocks, Brigge tried to pray and he thought of the candles in his house. This thought led him into a waking dream. He could see the candles very plainly, burning in the window, Elizabeth behind them, her face all deathly white. Then a huge gust came, the air was exploded and the flames were snuffed out. Through the gloom he saw Elizabeth in her white winding sheet, hands crosswise on her breast, with rosemary and rue in her fingers. A bell tolled as the women watched her, she was senseless and without motion, as still as the child beside her.

This vision passed before his eyes. There were shadows in the mist and the hairs on his arms and neck stood up.

When they were through the pass, they led the horses carefully down to the new bridge and the moor beyond. The snow continued to fall but it did not settle. The moor was vast, malevolent and borderless, and it claimed the water for itself, for the freezing black pools into which, in time, dogs and lambs and even men with their horses would innocently stray, slide and drown.

They came to the road which skirted the moor and led to the town. The coroner mounted his mare once more. He would have spurred her on, in the hope of outriding his dreams and presentiments, but the road was mud, stones and water. Progress, necessarily, was slow.

Ma – E-J Major <ej@digitaldreamworld.co.uk>

John Burnside
Blackbird

(*dream catcher*)

It's not the bird itself
but what it does

– the vanishing –
is what we come to learn
beyond the stillness
of a suburb dawn;

though nothing in the day
feels different:

the usual morning
        street trees   lighted yards
the noise of traffic   out beyond the point

and hanging in the grey
above our bed
a knot of wire and feathers
                scarlet twine

and crazing

Poetry

> *– they said we were born with souls*
> *and I thought of something paper white*
> *and empty, like the sweet communion host*
> *that melted on my tongue, and left no trace –*

and still, when the blackbird returns,
we step outside and leave the door ajar
the colour and scent of lilies blurring the walls
the shadow that stands in the hallway

> *– a song, a guide –*

sweeter by far than anything we know.

> (*in a green light*)

That history we never learned in school,
where things are born into their names
as easily as morning fills a room,

and sleep is deeper than the sleep we share
with trees and insects, deeper than the scent
that gusts along the coast road after rain.

And when we speak of once upon a time,
I always think a sound is all we have
to go on, like that echo in the well

behind the church: a secret memory
unfolding in our hearts, while we pursue
this other life, this common frequency.

We know the scent of lilac and the chill
of falling water; clouds above the town
and cradles stopped with salt, or herringbone.

We know a world
– and still we live untouched,
hiding our love in the dark, with rags and shells,

or thinking of the games we played
as children, in the green of afternoon,
tossing a ball back and forth, on an open field,

the air turning soft and cool above the park
the darkness seeping in
through autumn trees;

how, every time, we wanted to go on,
in tune with every move, alert and spare,
watching the ball as it travelled from hand to hand,

our bodies skilled and warming to a loss
as total and incomplete
as a blackbird's singing.

Biographical Notes

Lars von Trier See page 1 for details.

Peter Holm-Jensen grew up in Tanzania, Indonesia, Denmark and Canada. Now living in the UK, he is a postgraduate student at the British Centre for Literary Translation at the University of East Anglia. He translates from Danish to English, and is currently seeking to publish his translations of Inger Christensen's novel *Evighedsmaskinen* (*Perpetuum Mobile*) as well as Lars von Trier's manuscript and film diary *Idioterne* (*The Idiots*).

Claire MacDonald is a writer, curator and editor, living in Cambridge and Washington, DC, where she teaches writing for performance. She is a founding editor of the journal *Performance Research*. Her theatre texts include 'Storm from Paradise', 'An Imitation of Life' and 'Beulah Land', which she is now reworking as a novel.

Roger Garfitt was the 2001 writing fellow at UEA. His *Selected Poems* is published by Carcanet, and he is currently writing a memoir, *The Horseman's Word*, part of which is set in Norfolk.

George Szirtes was born in Budapest in 1948 and came to England as a refugee in 1956. His most recent books are *The Budapest File* (Bloodaxe, 2000) and *An English Apocalypse* (Bloodaxe, 2001). He is also a translator and critic, has won various prizes and is a Fellow of the Royal Society of Literature. Together with Penelope Lively he edited *New Writing 10* (Picador, 2000).

Biographical Notes

Jose Luis Padrón Plazoala See page 43 for details.

Amaia Gabantxo was born in a fishing village in the Basque country in 1973. She translates from Basque and Spanish into English, and is currently editing and translating an anthology of Basque writing for her Ph.D. thesis at the British Centre for Literary translation at UEA. Her translations of Bernardo Atxaga's love poetry have appeared in *Modern Poetry in Translation* and she is seeking publishers for several of her translation projects. Recently, she was awarded a Wingate Scholarship. One of her short stories was shortlisted for the Asham prize in 1999.

Georg Trakl (1887-1915) See page 47 for details.

Will Stone was born in 1966 and lives in Suffolk. He holds an MA in Literary Translation from the University of East Anglia (1999), where he has also been visiting translator. His translation of 'Les Chimeres' by Gerard de Nerval was published by the Menard Press in 1999. His translations of Trakl, Nerval and Baudelaire have appeared in the journals *Modern Poetry in Translation*, *Exchanges* and *The International Review*. He has published several pamphlets of poetry, and in 1996 his poems were exhibited on a Number 38 bus in London. He has recently been working on translations of poems by Egon Schiele and those of Gerhard Fritsch. His next project will be a translation of the poetry of Emile Verhaeren.

Raoul Schrott was born in 1964. he has won prizes for his collections of poetry, *Hotels* (1995) and *Tropen* (*Tropes*, 1998), but became something of a literary sensation/enfant terrible with the 1997 publication of *Die Erfindung der Poesie* (*The Invention of Poetry*) an anthology of 'poems from the first 4,000 years', which includes his translations of poems from Sumerian, Breton, Greek, Welsh among others. His reputation was cemented by a collection of polemical poetological essays (1999) and translations versions from a wide range of languages and genres etc., including the *Bacchae* for the Burgtheater, and a recent lyrical novel, *Die Wüste Lob Nor* (*The Lob Nor Desert*).

Iain Galbraith was born in Glasgow and educated at the universities of Cambridge, Freiburg and Mainz. Since his first book publication, *Britische Lyrik der Gegenwart* (1984), he has introduced the work of Scottish, English, Welsh and Irish poets in German periodicals, on radio and at poetry festivals, and has translated contemporary German and Austrian authors into English. His own poems and essays have appeared in many journals and books.

Sarah May is the author of *The Nudist Colony* (Vintage, 2000) and the forthcoming *Spanish City* (Chatto, 2002).

Mehmet Yashim was born in 1958 in Neapolis, Nicosia, in British Cyprus. He is a household name in Cyprus and Turkey, where he is best known for his prize-winning poetry collections. He has been described by critics as '. . . a rising star of contemporary Turkish poetry'. His first novel, *Pisces Your Bloodbrother*, was published in Turkey in 1994 and was awarded the prestigious Cevdet Kudret Novel Prize in 1995.

Ümit Hussein is of Turkish Cypriot origin and grew up bilingual, between two cultures. She has a degree in Italian and European Literature and an MA in Literary Translation from UEA. She has lived and worked in Spain, France, Italy, Tunisia and Japan and is about to move to Portugal.

Draco Maturana Romesin is a widely exhibited Chilean painter and sculptor as well as an engineer and psychologist. He stayed in Santiago throughout the military dictatorship. He and his wife retired to the island of Chiloe, in the south of Chile, where he sees his role as 'the artist as witness of his time'. This is his first short story to be published anywhere.

Biographical Notes

Penny Rendall has spent the last three years working full time to establish Tindal Street Press, of which she remains a director. She now hopes to spend more time on her own writing and translating. Her next project is to translate a proposed collection of Draco Maturana's stories. She lives mainly in Birmingham with her husband and sons, but spends part of every year in Spain and Latin America.

Neil Grimmett has had stories published in, amongst others, *London Magazine, Stand, Panurge, Iron, Ambit*, and *Sepia*. In the US, *Fiction* and *The Yale Review*, in Canada, *Grain*, in France, *Paris Transcontinental*, in Australia, *Quadrant*, in South Africa, *New Contrast*. First novel, *The Bestowing Sun*, just signed by agent Simon Trewin. Neil lives and writes in Chania, Crete with his wife Lisa.

Lawrence Norfolk was born in London in 1963. His novels include the bestsellers *Lemprière's Dictionary* (Minerva, 1992), *The Pope's Rhinoceros* (Minerva, 1997) and, most recently, *In the Shape of a Boar* (Weidenfeld, 2001).

Günther Kaip (1887-1915) See page 87 for details.

Mike Mitchell was formerly a lecturer at Stirling University with a special interest in modern Austrian literature, now a literary translator, mainly from German. Recent publications include: *Kokoschka: Plays and Poems, Kubin: The Other Side, Grimmelshausen: Simplicissimus and The Life of Courage, Helmut Krausser: The Great Bagarozy, Werner Schwab: An Anthology of Plays*.

Juan Goytisolo See page 101 for further details.

Peter Bush is Director of the British Centre for Literary Translation. He has translated over twenty novels and screenplays including work by Pedro Almodovar, Juan Carlos Onetti, Senel Paz and Luis Sepulveda. He also edited *The voice of the turtle: an anthology of Cuban stories* (Grove & Quartet). He is currently translating novels by Spanish writer, Nuria Amat, and Mexican writers, Carmen Boullosa and Ignacio Padilla.

Stefano Benni See page III for details.

Carol O'Sullivan is Associate Director of the British Centre for Literary Translation at the University of East Anglia. She is finishing a Ph.D. on translating modernism and translates contemporary Italian fiction.

Hannah Crow was born in 1966 in Somerset, and brought up in Cornwall. She attended St Mary's College, Twickenham, from 1984-1987 to study English and Drama. Hannah started writing in 1995 and was published in *First Fictions: Introduction 13* (Faber&Faber, 1996). Hannah's first novel *Lee Trebilcock In The Twentieth Century* was published by Anchor in 1999. She is currently living in Leeds.

Elisabeth Sheffield's short fiction has appeared in various literary magazines including *The Ledge*, *13th Moon*, *The Denver Quarterly* and *Gargoyle*, as well as the first volume of *Chick-Lit*, a publication of the Fiction Collective 2. Elisabeth has lived and taught in Germany, Northern Cyprus and on both coasts of the United States, as well as in-between. Currently, she is in Boulder, Colorado, finishing a novel.

Mairi Contos was born in Australia. She took degrees in English at Sydney University, and has been working in teaching. She came to the UK for the MA in creative writing at the UEA and is currently working on a collection of interlinked short stories.

Clare Birchall is 28. She teaches media studies and creative writing at the University of Sussex. She is represented by A.M. Heath and is working towards a collection of short stories. Her stories have appeared in the *Sunday Express Magazine* and an anthology by the Do-Not Press.

Paul Barron received an MFA degree and the Fred Meijer Fellowship in Creative Writing from the University of Michigan, where he is currently a lecturer. Originally from Newcastle-upon-Tyne, he lives in Michigan with his wife and son. He is completing a book of short stories set in Newcastle.

Biographical Notes

Christine Anne Thomas was born and raised on the island of Oahu, Hawaii, where she has also worked as a freelance journalist. She read English at the University of California at Berkeley and recently completed the MA in creative writing at UEA. Currently at work on a new novel, *The Lei Makers*, she also writes reviews for the *Times Literary Supplement*.

Ronan Bennett was brought up in Belfast and now lives in London. He is the author of three novels. The most recent, *The Catastrophist*, was shortlisted for the Whitbread novel award. His film screenplays include *Face* and *Lucky Break*, and, for television, *Rebel Heart* and *Love Lies Bleeding*.

John Burnside is Lecturer in Creative Writing at the University of St Andrews. He received his B.A. degree from Cambridgeshire C.A.T. and is a Fellow of the Royal Society of London. His areas of specialisation include creative writing, and American and Spanish-language literature, poetry and philosophy. His most recent publications include the novels *Mercy Boys* (2000) and *The Locust Room* (2001), and the collection of short stories *Burning Elvis* (2000), all published by Johnathan Cape.

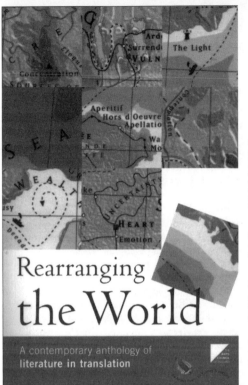

Also Available from Pen&inc:

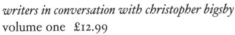

Back issues of *Pretext* direct from Pen&inc
(price includes p&p)

Volume One: Salvage £7.99
Ali Smith, Nell Dunn, Patricia Duncker,
Pagan Kennedy, David Almond.

Volume Two: Experience £7.99
Martin Amis, Lorna Sage,
Christopher Fowler, Andrew McGahan,
Peter Ho Davies, Alan Beard, Jackie Gay

Volume Three: Rancour £7.99
Toby Litt, Tim Parks, Edward Upward
Amy Prior, Mary Mann, Joel Lane

writers in conversation with christopher bigsby
volume one £12.99
Pen&inc have collaborated with the Arthur Miller
Centre to produce two volumes of interviews with
some of the world's most important and influential
literary figures.
volume one contains interviews with:
Edward Albee, Joseph Heller, Martin Amis,
Salman Rushdie, Margaret Atwood, Toni Morrison,
John Updike, Kurt Vonnegut, Don DeLillo.

writers in conversation with christopher bigsby
volume two £10.99
volume two contains interviews with: Paul Auster,
Joan Didion, John Fowles, W.G. Sebald, George
Steiner, Paul Theroux, Alice Walker, Arnold
Wesker, Tom Wolfe.

Stop Press!

News from Pen&inc:

Pretext Volume 5 will be edited by guest editor Ali Smith, author of **Hotel World** (Hamish Hamilton, 2001).

Volume 5 will be published in May 2002. To submit your work for publication please send an SAE for return of your material to Pretext Editors c/o Pen&inc, EAS, UEA, Norwich, NR4 7TJ.

With **Reactions2** already in the shops we are calling for submissions for Volume 3. Submissions are invited from writers who have had a first collection or pamphlet published (but not a second), and from those who have not yet reached that stage.

Is your poetry acid or alkaline? As long as it isn't neutral, we'd like to hear from you . . .

If you are interested in submitting work, please send five poems with an SAE to Esther Morgan at the School of English and American Studies, University of East Anglia, Norwich NR4 7TJ.

The poems you send:

- can be on any subject, in any style and of any length.
- should be written in English, but can be in translation.
- should be typed, with your name and address appearing clearly on each.
- must be your own original work.
- must not already be accepted for publication by any magazine (although poems which are due to appear in a first collection or anthology will be considered).
- should be accompanied by a covering letter which lists the titles of your poems, plus a short biography (of no more than 70 words).
- need to reach me no later than 31 March 2002.
- must be good.

The third edition of *Reactions* will appear in 2002. *Reactions* is a forum for new poetry by new poets.

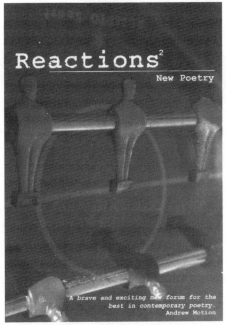

Reactions²
New Poetry

A brave and exciting new forum for the best in contemporary poetry.
Andrew Motion

Following up on the success of **Reactions** Volume 1, Volume 2 is another round-up of the best new poets from around the UK and abroad. Partly selected from open submission, and partly commissioned, **Reactions** features the work of poets who are at a first collection stage or working towards it.

Praise for Volume 1

'A stimulating and extraordinary collection.'
   Exhibit A

'A sticklebacked body of poetry.'
   The Big Issue

'What is remarkable about this volume is that poetry becomes a vehicle that breaks down language barriers, opens up fields of shared experience, stretching somewhere beyond.'
   The Times

Publication Date: October 2001 **ISBN:** 1-902913-12-4 **Size:** 250 pp **Price:** £7.99

Order Form
All prices include p&p

Pretext		Please tick	Quanti
Volume One: Salvage	£7.99	☐	☐
Volume Two: Experience	£7.99	☐	☐
Volume Three: Rancour	£7.99	☐	☐
Volume Four: Havoc	£4.50	☐	☐
Reactions Volume One	£7.99	☐	☐
Reactions Volume Two	£7.99	☐	☐
writers in conversation volume 1	£12.99	☐	☐
writers in conversation volume 2	£10.99	☐	☐
Total	£ ——		

Name: _____

Address: _____

Email: _____

Tel: _____

Please make all cheques payable to:
University of East Anglia
Send your order to:
Pen&inc,
English & American Studies,
University of East Anglia,
Norwich, NR4 7TJ